MW00659032

OFF THE COAST OF *Zanzibar*

By
Greg S. Reid

Sherpa Press

Off the Coast of Zanzibar by Greg S. Reid

Sherpa Press
2510 Warren Ave Suite 3898
Cheyenne, WY 82001
www.sherpapress.com

ISBN 978-0-9829850-2-1
Library of Congress Cataloging Data

OFF THE COAST OF *Zanzibar*

Appreciation

In addition to Summer Felix, special thanks and acknowledgement go out to all the leaders and dreamers who make this world a better place. They are always an example of service!

Introduction

Over the centuries, lessons have best been absorbed through parables and stories passed along from one generation to the next. This book continues that tradition with a modern-day tale that reinforces the strategies for personal and business success that have stood the test of time.

Throughout these pages, you will be reminded of age-old wisdoms, which may rekindle the entrepreneurial spirit that made this nation so great and that lies within you, ready to be shared with the world.

Enjoy and whatever you do.... Keep smiling!

Contents

Zanzibar

CHAPTER 1

No TURNING BACK

The plane landed at 9:40 p.m. at Kilimanjaro Airport. Karl Patrick, of average height and less than copious hair, walked off the plane. The breeze warmed his face and the feeling could only be described as one thing--Africa.

His assembly of hikers circled around. Most of them matched their profile picture of the group he signed up with to climb. He moved his way into the cluster with ease, reminding himself that while he appeared to be in decent shape, he would need to keep his own pace. After giving himself permission to just be, he introduced himself to the other eight hikers, maintaining the intention that it was more about the travel than the arrival.

Fans flurried above his head as he made his way behind the others through immigration. It was hot. He wondered for a moment, if he should rush ahead, but instead he brought himself back to the moment and enjoyed watching his climbing mates ahead. He thought of Liz back at home with their son. This was Jake's last summer at home before university. Their only son would soon be fleeing the nest. That thought alone increased the intensity of the heat as it rose from the wood floors. Karl's mind hummed a song as he prepared himself for the next five days. On his way to the baggage claim area, as the group separated to hunt for their own belongings, he felt the solitude and darkness magnify and he questioned his reasoning for including this adventure on his bucket list. Did anyone else feel the same isolation in the air? Or was this just another fear?

He retrieved his luggage and entered the van that awaited the hikers and one of the porters who came along to welcome them. He smiled and attempted brief moments of small chat, but mostly felt content or at least safe in his silence. He listened to the hikers tell stories of their children, their home life and what they did for a living. Most of them seemed adequately satisfied with their lives this far. They asked the older Tanzanian driver endless questions of their surroundings and they asked the porter to reassure them of their training. Karl had very little training except for vigorous hikes along the local trails in his hometown of Coos Bay, in the Portland metropolitan area where his well-known and reputable engineering firm was located. Over the years, strategic partnerships, school involvement and charities were woven into the life he created with his family.

The driver's broken English and the darkness of the road brought a yearning to hold his wife at home in their bed. But, the donkeys alongside the road and the people who walked with them renewed his excitement. The adventure had begun whether Karl was yet committed to it or not.

While the others agreed to gather for a midnight African beer, Karl spent his last night before the climb with his book and journal. Karl had certainly read excellent books in his life. Of these, a few stood out as hallmarks of learning, and repositories of wisdom. He always carried at least one with him. In its time, each book enabled him to develop and distinguish his personal life, business, as well as his business acumen, over the years and each book served as a reminder of where he was and how he got there.

The room had an aged wood smell. Karl set down his bags and looked around the room. The dresser resembled an antique like the kind his grandmother would have in the guest room. He walked to the bathroom and glimpsed himself in the mirror. This was it. He stretched his tired body into the semi-comfortable reclining chair and considered his life journey thus far and how he made it to this moment today and how he would make it through the coming days. The climb. He observed himself as a reflection of the books he's read and the people he has met, all of which carried messages that impacted his life. He pulled out a fresh brown leather tied journal and opened it up. He bent it around to give it more flexibility and imagined how nimble it might be by the end of this trip.

Here it was. The biggest physical feat he had yet attempted. Part of him felt satisfied enough with what he had seen to turn back, grab the next flight out and go home to his family. The other part of him felt ecstatic to make the phone call to Liz, to announce, "I did it, baby." He wanted to make more of those phone calls and he knew that feeling well.

Should he mingle with the other hikers? Maybe. But, there was peace in the small, pinkish colored hotel room and he wanted to savor the moments leading up to his first and last dreams before he embarked.

The others seemed so calm along the ride. He didn't catch all of their names. He wondered if they are nervous like him. Did they hide it well? There was fear within him, but it was accompanied by fearless adrenaline. He had experienced this feeling before. Be it a physical venture or business venture, the feeling remained the same. Holy crap! What was he about to do? Did he have any business at all taking on such a climb? Most of these people have done some sort of a climb before. Or at least he gathered as much from the car ride to the hotel. What were their names again? He felt like a complete novice. Then he remembered one thing he brought that he could use and leave at the hotel to pass on to someone else. His indispensable guide, *Think and Grow Rich,* by Napoleon Hill. He knew he would need it. Right now it served as a reminder. A go get 'em speech. Of all times, he needed to remember his minds' capacity to understand and relate with people. It was the something that had held him back and when given the right attention was the means to his victories. It was a skill that needed improvement and it was the bigger reason of this climb's importance. *Think and Grow Rich* was the book that enabled him to regard new philosophies of principles where he could transcend his hang-ups about success and learn how to achieve the goals he most desired. Climbing Kilimanjaro was, indeed, a goal he most desired. After all, it was on his bucket list.

Karl drifted off to sleep with the book at his side. He tossed and turned a few times awakened by loud animal fights, the lowing of the cows, and lingering anticipation, knowing there was no turning back.

Zanzibar
CHAPTER 2

Trust THE EXPERIENCE

After a fairly recognizable breakfast meal, Karl got on the bus with the other hikers. During the two-hour ride, most of the hikers were silent. It was a clear shift from the excitement the night before. The rough road and dirt, now visible in bright sunlight, had the crew deep in thought. Karl wondered what each mind was processing as their eyes stared out the window. Were they, like him, seeking a little something extra? Was this a vehicle for them to make a life decision? Was it an escape? Was it just a physical or emotional challenge for them? Questions flooded his mind. One after the other. He didn't know whether he truly cared for their answers or was seeking his own reasoning. Through all the challenges he faced; through the falls and the triumphs, he asked for more challenges. He learned from each one, but still questioned a greater purpose. Did the other hikers feel the same?

He met all of them briefly, but could only remember a few of their names. There was a couple, Jan and Nathan. They were in their mid-fifties, like Karl, and had a history of adventure behind them with no signs of retiring. This was just another notch on their belt of escapades.

There was Joyce, a taller woman who seemed to be very intelligent without having to say much. Karl sensed a greater meaning to this climb for her, other than a test of cardiovascular endurance or expressive breakdowns.

Ruthe, who carried a vivacious energy about her even in silence, had a story written in her eyes. What did the climb mean for her? He wondered what it was about most of them that brought them here, now seriously questioning his own reasons while returning his attention to the window.

The van led them to the Machame Gate where the hike would begin. Upon arriving, each person signed in and prepared for the climb. For most, that meant eating a good lunch. Karl watched as the women rushed to the stand up toilets to relieve themselves. While he wasn't expecting the beginning to be the difficult part, it was still the beginning of a great challenge he anticipated based on his readings.

Everyone looked to have left fear and deep thought in the van and toilets. Everyone except Karl. He fleetingly wished that he was at the crux of the hike so as to quell his anxiety. It was like that impetuous urge to jump up and volunteer to go first during oral book reports in the ninth grade just to end his anxiety. Suddenly, Karl's heart pounded faster than he could remember. The funny thing about anxiety was that it never seemed to compare to any other moment and this moment certainly stood out from the rest. He needed relief; something that would help him to pull himself together so he could trust that everything would be just as it should be. He didn't want to just get it over with. He wanted to enjoy it. And in that very moment, he remembered Steven.

While everyone enjoyed packed sandwich lunches and cookies, Karl found a rock where he could sit and unite with the calm in him that would allow him to trust. He pulled out his journal and let the nervous energy vacate through his fingers as he wrote three words on a blank page.

Trust the Experience

He had met Steven Kaufman on his long-anticipated trip to France, at a small village motel in the countryside. Another "to do" on his bucket list. He was traveling with a small group of friends, and Steven was on a solo bicycling trip, preparing for the Tour de France. They met at dinner, when he saw Steven eating alone, and invited him to join him and his friends. He recalled the distinct look of confidence and ease as he sat alone, then joined them to eat. Something about an inner strength he carried compelled Karl to reach out to him, perhaps because at the time he was searching for this same quality inside himself.

As Steven talked about his life-long interest in bicycling and racing, Karl felt inspired by his motivation and bravery to pursue something so intently, and told him so.

That's when Steven exclaimed, "When you're living fully in the moment, great things happen!"

Karl couldn't help but laugh at the extreme excitement in his voice. He asked, "Are you talking about something like *carpe diem,* seize the day?"

Steven got a glimmer in his eyes and said to Karl, "Listen my friend, I am saying that when you become inspired by something, trust the experience. Too often we let moments go by that have the capacity to really awaken us to something profound about ourselves and our situation in life. When you are fully attuned to the moment, to this ongoing moment in which we all live, then you will find a tremendous source of inspiration. And when you do, you've got to trust it. That's how I came to race in the Tour de France."

At that time in his life, when Karl was still finding the balance of work and enjoyment, Steven brought him to realize that in both his personal and business endeavors he was reluctant to trust at all. He held onto suspicions and uncertainties that kept him from fully committing to doing and getting what he wanted. He wasn't trusting his own experiences. Karl had just ended a relationship with a woman who marveled at his ability to relate to others and yet wasn't able to completely relate to her. He often cited that his lack of connection came from his lack of trust. As hard as she tried, she couldn't break him.

"When people don't trust the experience of living in the moment, they dismiss a large portion of their greatness," Steven continued. "Because who we are is so much more than the habitual dialogues in our heads. Who we are is a living mystery filled with potential, wonder and awe. Because we are alive right now!"

It seemed like Steven was trying to wake Karl from a perpetual unconscious slumber he had learned to inhabit for a long time. He knew that dialogue all too well. It was the dialogue that kept him in the safe zone for so long.

"Think of the times you surrendered yourself to the moment," he added. The impact of his words were like a gigantic bird hammering upon the human-sized eggshell that surrounded Karl, trying to break through and rescue him from an overly-protected and controlled way of life.

"Yep. I think I understand what you're talking about." Steven had an expression of amusement and slight exasperation. Steven told him a story that still sits with him, "A few years ago, I got married, and my wife and I went to Greece for our honeymoon. After our first day of seeing the sights, we wanted to eat at an authentic Greek restaurant. The honeymoon was a barrage of ill events and all we wanted was a nice dinner. We got directions from the hotel manager, but ended up getting lost, and finally made our way to what looked like a dingy, hole-in-the-wall restaurant. When we walked in, the only person there was a little old woman. She could see we were hungry and confused as she sat us at a table. We weren't looking to eat there. We just needed some help. But, we sat down anyway. Although she didn't speak much English, she said "Trust me," and went back into the kitchen. About fifteen minutes later, my wife and I were enjoying one of the most delicious meals we've ever had."

"The truth is, we had ended up at the authentic Greek restaurant we were looking for without even knowing it," Steven continued. "It wasn't just about good food. It was the connection we made with the woman. It was finally feeling good on a vacation that wasn't going so smoothly. It was that switch in our untrusting minds that created a whole new experience for us that we return to time and time again."

Karl got it. They surrendered themselves into the moment instead of resisting it. Countless memories of times with Liz at unlikely places created the best moments, but he didn't know at the time he would have those experiences. Meeting Steven opened him up to the opportunity.

Steven went on, "We continue to scan our bodies, our relationships, our finances, and our lives for 'what's wrong' versus trusting the experience we are living. In both your business and your personal life, you can never fully understand or predict what you are getting yourself into. Always use common sense, and trust your instincts. But, also have trust. If you trust your experiences the way my wife and I trusted the old woman in the restaurant, you will always have the very best results."

The entire experience meeting Steven was so awakening for Karl that he wished it could have gone on longer that night. The next day, Steven continued on his bicycling trek, and Karl went on with his.

This day was no different. Karl looked at the others and observed how they were in this. They were absorbed in getting to know each other, laughing together, and they were engaged. They were truly in this. He realized that he was exactly where he was supposed to be because it was exactly where he was in this moment.

He took a deep breath and took note once again of the surreal panorama surrounding him and joined in with the others. He confronted the reality of what was happening; putting aside any thoughts of what should be happening and he surrendered himself to the experience. The energy was there. He was ready.

CHAPTER 3

Shoop

Day 1
Start: Machame Gate, approx 6,000 feet
Terrain: Rainforest, plentiful vegetation with occasional rain
Duration: 5 hours
End: Machame Camp, approx. 9,850 feet:

One of the climbers, who was quite talkative when they arrived, started to seem less enthused. Feeling less nervous himself, Karl decided to walk over and talk to the suddenly timid young guy.

"You alright?" Karl tried to not to invade his space, but wanted to give him some comfort at the same time.

"Ah, just a little anxious, I guess." Karl could tell he was trying to hide his discomfort.

"Yeah, I know what you mean. I keep going back and forth with nerves and doubt." They both nodded. "I'm Karl, by the way."

"Right, yeah I remember you as the quiet one on the ride over. Little table turn now, huh?" He laughed nervously. "I'm Jacob." He reminded Karl of his son. Young, kind and not a hundred percent fearless as most would predict from his athletic build.

"You remind me of my son, only taller. He loved basketball and always wished he had the extra height like you."

"Funny. I actually never got into basketball."

"No?"

"Nah, billiards and darts were more my thing."

"Is that so?"

"Yup." Jacob started to loosen up and it was helping Karl to relax as well, at least temporarily.

"So, I learned this philosophy from a good friend and sometimes when I feel uncomfortable about where I'm at, I reflect on it and it usually helps."

Jacob seemed to respond to Karl's efforts. "Yeah? What's that?"

"Well, about ten years back I was working as an installer for storm windows. The whole green building notion was starting to become more popular with homes and I happened to be good at it, seeing as how I was always in the contracting and building business."

Jacob kept listening.

"Well, even though I was good at it, I knew I didn't want to keep working for someone else forever. Eventually, I wanted to venture out on my own. And it was at that time that I met a guy that has become one of my closest buddies. His name is J. And to this day, whenever I feel scared about a change in my life, whether it's physically, emotionally or mentally challenging – I just SHOOP."

Jacob laughed. "Shoop?"

"Shoop. It's blending five simple strategies to get you to that middle target – to the bull's eye."

"Like darts?"

"Uh-huh."

"So, what, if I may ask, are these strategies and where does the 'shoop' come in? Because right now, all I can picture is a dance."

Karl laughed at the notion. "Shoop is J's name. J. Shoop. And he developed these five steps that till this day have helped keep me on target with my goals and eliminate the obstacles that get in my way. Things like fear and doubt."

Jacob turned to face Karl more directly. In that moment, Karl went right back to that first day J. introduced him to the Shoop concept.

Karl had just finished a job and met J. for dinner. After expressing his stagnant feeling about work, J. suggested his theory. "There are five things you've got to nail down when it comes to yourself and how you live your life, Karl. Once you've got those steps down. Bam! You hit your target, which is your purpose, your "why." So many people get stuck because they never determine what their purpose is and even more importantly, they have no clue how to *figure out* what it is."

"What's my purpose, J?!" Karl was eager now and said only half-jokingly. He was at that point where he felt stuck. He didn't know what he was working towards or why.

J. began, "Well, let's start with the S. Success philosophy. You've got to ask yourself, what is your personal success philosophy? Most of us operate on a premise of what success means to us, whether we are aware of it or not. Sometimes we model other people's behavior and that means success for us. But, try looking deeper and really considering what success looks and feels like for you. Does it mean more free time? Does it mean more money? Does it simply mean that you're alive?" He chuckled a bit. "Decide what it means for you. You'll notice a release in tension all over when you nail it. Once you've consciously adopted a success philosophy that resonates and that you can apply to your life, then move on to step two."

"Which is?" Karl eagerly questioned.

"H."

"Oh, right of course. H!" Karl laughed. "And H is?"

"Habits. What are your habits Karl? And which ones support your vision of success and which make you take a step back? We become what we repeatedly do, so if what we keep doing isn't working, maybe it's time to find new habits that will reinforce positive outcomes."

"Isn't it hard to suddenly change your habits?"

"And there's your third one, Karl."

"What?"

"Outlook. Nothing has to be that hard. If we change our outlook and perception then it can be as hard as we make it or as easy as we make it. It's up to you. You have the power to choose the perception that will support your new philosophy of success."

"You do make it sound simple. In fact, every time I am with you things seem easier."

"That brings me to the second O and the fourth step. Other people."

"Other people?" Karl asked.

"You know as well as I do, Karl, that change brings about discomfort to those around and they can start to bring us down. This is the time we search for new associations with those who can recognize and realize the same things that are important to us. What drives the people you hang out with? What are their motives? Look at them and then look at yourself. Associate with the people who match your vision of success and you will arrive there."

Karl nodded. "You know J., I hadn't even thought about what success would look like. I didn't even take notice of the habits I had until you brought this up. In just this bit of time, I know exactly what my success looks like and I can clearly see how my habits, outlook and some other people in my life aren't serving that goal. I think I just realized something pretty profound."

"And?"

"I think I just Shooped myself a purpose."

"Bingo. That's your target!" He pointed out, "The P in Shoop represents your purpose. The funny thing is, you can actually have some success without uncovering your true purpose. But until you do, you'll never quite reach the levels of success that you are capable of – or that you deserve. Most of us aren't missing the target entirely, but we're not necessarily hitting the bull's eye either. The key is to continue working to identify your 'why'. Karl recalled it was at this moment he got a sense of his own why: to provide for his family by being a part of the budding environmental movement.

Jacob listened while Karl reflected back on his friend J. "Wow, that's pretty cool, Karl. You know I wasn't quite sure why I was doing this at all. But, that's such a simple way to remind me of where I'm going and to keep my focus on discovering my true purpose."

"Think you're ready to take on this climb now?"

"Better believe it!"

"Good. I'm hanging out with you then!"

Karl walked up to the rest of the group just behind Jacob and gave silent thanks to his friend J. who had helped him discover his why and again helped someone else through a challenging moment.

Honest EYES

Karl was feeling optimistic until another challenge came along. The speech and education before heading out was not something a fearful hiker would want to hear. It didn't quite lure anyone to take this climb. In fact, it almost pushed Karl back. Man, did he need to wake that giant. Whenever he felt that pull to sit out, he remembered one of his favorite books-- Tony Robbins' *Awakening The Giant Within.* It was the book that helped Karl to identify the shortcomings in his attitude and his behaviors, as well as to change them for the better. It opened up his potential to interact more effectively with co-workers and clients and women. Now he needed it to open and interact with the hikers, and the mountain itself. He needed the courage.

"So, what brought you here?" She said this while snapping a candid shot of Karl's first reaction to her. Her camera was very impressive and quite heavy looking for such a climb. Karl knew instantly that photography had to be important to her. Joyce Alzona was one of the first hikers in the group to talk to Karl once they embarked. She had a lot of energy as she spoke, walked and took pictures of the plush rainforest. He couldn't imagine her energy would fade at anytime. Despite his promise to maintain his own pace, he was finding it very easy to keep up with Joyce. They walked side by side, filling the footprints of the guides in front of them.

"Bucket list," Karl said just slightly out of breath and adjusting to the humidity in the air.

"This is on your list?" She smiled.

Karl could tell she appreciated that he had a bucket list. "Yep. And I'm hoping I don't regret it."

She laughed. "Ah, c'mon. You won't regret it. You're already committed right?"

"I guess so."

"You guess so? I got news for you. You're doing it! So, you better be committed."

Karl nodded and refreshed himself on how important it was to reunite with the lessons he'd learned about himself in life and to bring back more lessons from this trip. His practice had always been to apply them to his work and his life. Climbing to the top of Mount Kilimanjaro, he realized he needed to feel that commitment in order to conquer any remaining fears.

Without saying much yet, Karl could feel the inner strengths and capabilities of this woman. Her eyes were honest and took in everything that surrounded them. With no makeup on, dressed in unrevealing hiking gear and about three hours away from really needing a shower, he couldn't help but be drawn to her.

"I used to be so afraid of everything." She seemed to be in another place and took immediate comfort in talking to Karl. As they pressed on walking, he just listened, happy that he didn't have to ask a thing. "Then I realized that my success lived inside my fear," she continued. Karl became a little more interested at those words.

"You have to run towards your fears, go into the lions' roar of your fears in order to overcome them and find success. If you run from your fears, they will hunt you down like a lion who knows that you're avoiding him. But if you go right into the fear, you'll find the gift of your strength, which will enable you to accomplish what you desire. Just go all in."

Her face lightened up even more and she smiled as she walked on.

Karl didn't need to say anything to Joyce. But, she knew and he knew that he had just received a gift. Whether it was a reminder at the right time or something completely new, it was accepted.

"What do you do?"

"Well, I'm a professional photographer."

"Right, I should have guessed." He rolled his eyes as she clicked her camera for another blunt shot.

"But!" she continued, "Metaphorically, I create beauty and warmth in people's living environments, whether at home or at work. I help people to transform their lives by letting them see the beauty in their own lives through photographs. It's kind of like handing them a pair of reality-based, rose-colored glasses. So many people don't know what they have until they see it through someone else's eyes."

"Ha! That makes sense."

"For me, it's about getting people to feel more comfortable, engaged and energized with what's going on in their lives so that they feel more connected, creative and capable. Like you." She said this looking ahead and avoiding eye contact with Karl.

He couldn't help but respond, "Like me?"

"Uh huh."

"Was I uncomfortable and not capable?"

"Sorta, yeah."

"Am I still?"

"Nah, not since I told you to run towards the lions. I think that broke you in a bit, yeah?" Her voice was trying a little harder to keep up with her breath.

He chuckled in disbelief. "Well, yeah, I guess so."

"You're also walking a little faster now. I don't know if you noticed that."

"I did. Thank you. So, did my lungs."

"Well, we'll be resting soon. But, you're doing a great job."

Joyce's words came as a kind of uncanny wisdom that Karl didn't get from many other people. He knew her photographs would reflect the same. It was quickly giving him just enough fuel to break loose from the grip that his fears, and his resistance of reality, sometimes took upon him.

As the next resting point came, Joyce went to the others to get group photos. Karl watched them laugh and fed off of the energy they all had. Feeling solidly attuned with his personal mission, Karl opened his journal and took a moment to silently appreciate all he'd learned from Joyce.

Honest Eyes

He was already learning from this incredible adventure. He smiled and knew that he was prepared to continue his journey, wherever it might take him and hopefully to answer that lingering question inside.

Zanzibar

CHAPTER 5

Shallow PEOPLE HAVE SHALLOW BREATHS

Day 2
Start: Machame Camp, 9,258 feet
Duration: 6 hours
Terrain: Heath and moorlands
End: Shira Camp, approx. 12,467 feet

Since arriving, Karl couldn't help but feel like he was on "Survivor". Especially after the first night spent at the Machame Camp at 3000m, where the sleeping arrangements were nothing like the comfortable bed he had slept in just the night before. Everything in his business life was so intently based on the relationships he formed. After installing storm windows for so many years, Karl took advantage of the relationships he made with each project. Had it not been for his diligence with maintaining those relationships, his start up green building business would not have flourished. Yes, like on "Survivor", these relationships were for survival. But, suddenly he felt like his fight-or-flight survival mode was in a whole other gear. And they'd barely gotten started. It was just the beginning of day two of the seven-day trek. This morning the group was briefed that each day would bring on a different hiking terrain. They were also taught the Swahili term: Pole Pole which meant "slow down". The entire team was surprised at the first steps they had to take: steep rocky incline. It was a startling contrast to the gentle walk they took through the rainforest just the day before. Sure enough, the climate was beginning to change.

Through changing and challenging times, relationships were always key. It brought his thoughts to Dale Carnegie's *How to Win Friends and Influence People.* The communication strategies in this book enabled him to get his business message across the foreboding chasm between himself and the world, a chasm he thought he'd never forge. The book allowed him to feel much more free and easy when interacting with people at work, whether it's in the pressure cooker of intense business negotiations, or just over the course of a simple pitch to potential clients. It wasn't a bad idea to implement some of those skills on the mountain. He definitely wanted to be liked on this trip.

Karl assumed that the climbing wouldn't be too bad at first. He knew it would be fairly easy and not much different from the trails back at home. Then he reflected on the brochures and stories of others he read and realized that there were two different kinds of stories to be told. Those you tell after experiencing the climb and those that were accurate. The first day was just humid. The exertion wasn't enough to stop him from conversation or to slow down. What mostly captured Karl's attention were the wobbly-legged hikers coming down who smiled with support and attempted cheers, but had unoccupied eyes. It piqued his curiosity and fear. Why were their eyes so vacant?

So far, everyone was feeling great. Energy was high and appetites were healthy.

But as day two progressed, the efforts increased and it showed. The feeling that his body had been transported to an adverse environment was consistently overpowering him as well as yesterday's over-enthused climbers. There was no longer room enough for two to walk side by side. The path had narrowed and the group had to file into a single line as the ascent continued.

Phurba, one of the porters, shouted behind to go slow. "Pole! Pole!" Going slow wasn't the problem for Karl. It was the new air. In the thin air his breathing and his symptoms matched those he had read about.

It was time to eat and to rest again. The view from the camp was breathtaking. The team would be sleeping just a hair above the clouds for the night. Besides the clouds, the only other object within the line of sight was the top of Mt. Meru, the second highest mountain in Africa. As he forced down two bites of food despite his full day's climb and desperate need for fuel, Karl knew he was experiencing the onset of altitude sickness.

Everyone was tired. They sat in their respective rest areas and arranged themselves as comfortably as they could for a night at the Shira campsite, where the altitude hit just shy of 12,500 feet. Karl pulled out his journal with shaky hands and heavy eyes. As his breath became shallower, he remembered Margaret Ziedin. He opened his journal to a new blank page and wrote,

Shallow People Have Shallow Breaths

He remembered the overcast day he met her. After being cooped up in the house for too long, he knew it was time to walk down to the waterfront for fresh air. As he walked in the autumn chill, he smelled the changing aromas of a new season. Approaching the bay, he watched as a huge white cruise ship departed to set forth into the open waters. He sat at one of his favorite spots on a bench and listened to the seagulls as they pranced on the pier searching for scraps of food.

Karl enjoyed the surrounding scenery of the bay as much as he could keep present, but soon found himself sinking deeper into other thoughts. At this time, he knew he had some important decisions to make. All in all it had been a tough year, and he was feeling compelled to change the way he was living. As he sat thinking, the pressure of his thoughts built until they impelled him to stand up and walk around some more to release the anxious energy. The shops that lined the waterfront drew him. They were relatively vacant that cloudy day.

Not knowing why, he found himself specifically drawn into an eclectic boutique art shop by the magnificent display of sculptures, paintings and supplies. As he brushed off his shoes and the sound of the bells from the door opening faded, he noticed he wasn't the only customer. He was instantly greeted by the store clerk and also by a bright-eyed woman who was purchasing oil paints. He accepted their greetings and was feeling the urge to make an excuse for why he had come into the store, not having any need for supplies. But, the friendly atmosphere put the guilt at ease. The lady finishing her purchase asked him how his day was going, and while Karl would normally respond with a generic, "Good, thank you and yours?" He shrugged and told her that it was an interesting day. She was clearly not one to accept this for a final answer. She pressed on in a very concerning way and for some reason he opened up about how he was deliberating changes in his life and career.

The woman introduced herself as Margaret, and, as though she knew exactly how he was feeling, she started to tell him about a similar time in her life. She told him that as a youth she had felt disillusioned with her life and had dropped out of school. "I was looking for something to make me feel happy, or maybe just more alive; but I didn't know what it was," she told Karl. "But, finding a job was easy for me, because I was so hungry for new experiences and could easily convince employers of my capabilities. Sometimes, I would even work a day or two for free just to show them that I could do the job."

Karl felt pleasantly surprised to be having such a nice conversation with a new person. "That's really amazing," he replied.

Margaret smiled, and for a moment looked a bit shy. Then she proceeded to share with him the larger story of her life. "It's been a long time since those days," she laughed. "And I feel as if I've lived a few different lives since then." Her mood had lightened Karl considerably as he stood listening.

She told him that she had gotten married at a young age, eager to find someone with whom she could feel safe and secure, and most of all, loved. "But, that relationship turned out to be something of a dead end, because my husband and I had different views on what really living meant. After some time, I realized my dreams of adventure in the world were dying with him. He was complacent in a regular routine. For myself, I found that to be uninteresting. So, eventually, I left and quenched my craving for adventures."

"That must have been tough for you at such a young age," he replied.

"Yes, it was" Margaret agreed. "But, it was better than the alternative of living a stagnant and unfulfilling life." She went on to describe how she felt no resentment towards her ex-husband, but that she realized what was important to her was not important to him. "Our failed marriage was no one's fault," she told him. "Either you can stay and suffer with those around you that don't share your dreams, or you can have the courage to move on."

Karl was impressed with her wisdom. He really felt that he was in the same sort of situation with his job. "Sometimes the allure of security and predictability keeps me involved in life situations that I should probably move on from," he admitted to Margaret. "How do you find the courage to move on from situations that aren't really good for you?"

Margaret smiled again and laughed a bit, saying, "Well it isn't always easy! At some point in my life, I asked myself what I really wanted, and what I was willing to do to get what I wanted."

Karl exhaled. "I think for a long time I've felt driven to do things because I had to survive. I've stayed in relationships because it seemed easier. I'm in a job right now that pays the bills."

"Well, it's got to be about more than that Karl. Does it pay you?" Margaret quickly injected. "It's important to find a sense of purpose and meaning for your life. Something that really lights your spirit on fire, and gets you going each day."

As he took it in completely, he drew in a deep breath and let out a longer sigh.

"Just like that," Margaret affirmed.

"Just like what?" he retorted in confusion.

"You just took a really deep breath," she asserted. "That's the beginning of feeling what you feel, bringing in new life and letting go of fear."

"Really?" he said, feeling even more perplexed.

"Yes, of course," Margaret smiled. "Shallow breaths are for shallow people. The more fully you are able to breathe in life, the more deeply you will feel yourself to be alive." As Karl stood in front of Margaret, virtually digesting what she had said, she continued, "When you inhale you bring in the power that you need, and when you exhale you give freely of the universal energy that we all share."

Seeing that he was looking at her with very wide eyes, Margaret proclaimed, "The only way you'll overcome your fears is to take action, Karl. You've got to eat your fear for dinner!"

He laughed. "It seems you have quite a lot to teach me about my own life." At this he paused, then asked her, "So how did you learn so much about these things?"

"In truth, it all comes down to being honest," Margaret replied. "When you're honest with yourself and the world, you will be in a pure light and gain a sense of personal power. And when you are truly honest," she went on, "you become more attractive to other people in business, and all your relationships. When this happens, the people you really need will appear in your life."

"I guess being totally honest requires a lot of courage. I don't know if I'm cut out for it," he said, chuckling.

"After some practice, it becomes more of a regular way of life," Margaret replied. "Feeling vulnerable gives you permission to ask for help. And being authentic with others gives you a sense of ownership over your life. If you are true to yourself, and stand in your own truth; what can go wrong?"

"I guess maybe you're right" he said. "I'm just not sure how to do it."

"All you have to do is have the courage to be yourself. Like when you walked into this art shop," Margaret said.

"You could tell I was a bit awkward?"

"Yes, I could. People can be embarrassed about what attracts them. But you had the courage to come in and be honest with me, a total stranger, about your life. Then you had the courage to listen to me talk about my experiences. When you have courage, you find power because you are tapping into the source of who you are. That's why we attract what we need."

"Well, I'm definitely attracted to everything you're saying!" he exclaimed. "I realize I need to get more honest with myself and make some profound changes in the life I'm living."

He thanked Margaret for their conversation and as he said goodbye, he bought a still life painting of a basket filled with bright red apples.

Karl brought himself back to the moment, biting an apple. Even though his appetite was decreasing, he knew he needed the fuel. He took another deep breath and smiled thinking of Liz. After meeting Margaret, Karl made the decision that was lingering for a while and he quit his job of installing storm windows that had became unfulfilling. Just weeks later, he started up the business that would bring him both challenges and rewards. Karl's *Sustainable Sources, Inc.* opened for business. It was also at this time that he met Liz.

His so far momentous expedition to the top of Mount Kilimanjaro was granting Karl a greater insight into his own capabilities, as well as recognition of his untapped strengths. Following this enormous exertion, he planned a relaxing vacation on Zanzibar where he would call his wife and tell her of his journey. He didn't expect such a physical demand and he still had four days to go. Something about his tired bones and achievement thus far gave him a renewed appreciation for simply being human.

Zanzibar
CHAPTER 6

Bitter or Better: YOU CHOOSE

Day 3
Start: Shira Camp, 12,467 feet
Terrain: Alpine desert region,
Stop at the Lava Tower, at 15,220 feet
for an hour to adjust to altitude
Duration: 5 hours
End: Barranco Camp, 13,070 feet:

It was day 3. The bananas he brought turned brown. Karl was struck by the avoidance of the misery talk from the others. He thought, surely, someone would have a complaint. Could it be that people were slapping their own hands for having chosen this journey? Or it could it be that they were all experiencing the same confusion and delirium that Karl was? Or could it be that they just pushed through it and it wasn't much of a challenge for them as it felt to him?

This was an experience full of awe and yet, still, tragically awful. Karl at least appreciated the silence rather than any forced jolly optimism. Not that he was feeling pessimistic. No, he was too exhausted to have negative thoughts. But, the fantasies of a vacation afterward were heavily weighed.

The day's walk continued through the alpine desert region and all the way up to the Lava tower at 4600m. After hitting the Lava tower, the group would descend to Barranco camp at 3900m, where they would camp for the night. While some hikers would be frustrated at the ascent and then descent back to nearly the same level as the day before, it was necessary to reach their destination. Before long, the descent would be greatly appreciated as the ability to adjust to the air would be much easier.

As the gang finished breakfast, or what they could get down anyway, Karl noticed one woman he hadn't yet spoken to. She was looking at Karl and smiled when he caught her eye. As he got to his feet and placed his backpack back on his tired self, he noticed her walking towards him.

"I'm Ruthe St. Pierre." She held out her hand.

"I'm Karl."

"I know. We hadn't yet spoken and it's been quite a few days. Thought I'd introduce myself. How you hangin' in?"

"Ah, ya know. Same as you I guess?"

"Yeah. It's not easy. So, what brings you here?"

Karl pulled out his list from his bag's pocket and handed it to her.

"A bucket list. Commendable. You don't have much left on there. Looks like a magnificent life."

"You could say that. So, what about you? What brings you here?"

"Well, to make a short story long . . . ." She stopped and looked at him. "We have the time right?"

"I'd love to hear," Karl responded.

"There's been some rough roads in my life and every now and then I like to be reminded that there are those I get to choose and it's what I make of the challenges."

"I'm with ya on that one."

"And so here we are."

Karl and Ruthe talked right into the next massive ascent. It didn't take long for Ruthe to tell her story.

"I founded a family business and it had been a successful enterprise until a sudden family tragedy. I wasn't expecting such misfortune. I never suffered too much in my life until it happened."

She didn't offer to explain what happened and Karl didn't ask.

"My business suffered too. It was the joy in my life and it was diminishing rapidly. I gave up hope, and was in a very dark place of despair. It seemed so unjust. So unfair. At least that was my attitude."

"Most of us have been there, right?"

"And a lot of us stay there when we don't have to. I didn't get that at the time. I was so depressed. I ended up losing the business."

"Oh, I know that what that's like." Karl sighed. Just the thought of it, brought Karl back to a time when he just about lost everything after quitting his job to start his own business. Despair didn't even touch the emotions he had.

"I was completely fragmented inside, which became more evident as the life around me crumbled to pieces. I felt as if I had been cursed by life. I began taking long walks alone. I was seeking some kind of answer as to why my life had come to such a disastrous conclusion. Then late one day as I was coming to the pinnacle of a little hike, I knelt down to the earth and cried for what seemed like every last tear my body could hold."

"And you were struck." Karl had this feeling before. It was right at the time he felt he had no choice but to file for bankruptcy. Everything he worked so hard for came to halt because of one risky transaction. It was the bottom. It jeopardized his relationship with Liz. It put an end to their plans, at least it seemed at the time. It felt as if the world was caving in until suddenly he was struck like Ruthe.

Ruthe's eyes lit up and she nodded. Anyone else would think she just walked out of a rejuvenation spa not a mountain. "Yes! It was as if someone had thrown a rock, shattering the invisible shield of grief and bitterness that surrounded my heart." She was so excited. She sounded almost poetic to Karl. But, he got it. It was as if she was reliving the moment right then and there and he was experiencing it with her. He knew this feeling.

She continued on, lost in her own reverie. "Crouching there on the ground, in the day's last rays of sunlight, the spirit inside me broke free again. I became very aware of the present moment, and realized there was no turning back the clock. With every cell in my body I suddenly knew that, although the beautiful memories of happiness before the tragedy would always be with me, the past was gone, and all that was left is this very instant, this one living precious moment. Then it occurred to me that my life was still worth living, because I was still alive."

Karl nodded as he took the next step. The path was narrowing again and soon their conversation would end. Ruthe filed in front of him and said, "When people asked me how I recovered, I tell them I chose to become better instead of remaining bitter!"

It was that simple for Ruthe. All the time spent agonizing was altered in a moment. Karl had the same experience. It was a choice.

On the next rest stop at the Barranco Camp, Karl thought of the two words Ruthe said and the one letter that differentiated them.

Bitter or Better – You Choose

Karl spent much of his early years focusing on himself and what his own problems were and why he was entitled to more. It was when he started focusing on everyone and everything that would actually serve his purpose, he learned that something potentially debilitating could actually be something of inspiration to others and to himself. It was a fantastic reminder.

Through this exchange, Karl felt more inspired himself. As the previous days drained him of not only physical energy, but mental acuteness and enthusiasm, Ruthe's experience reminded him of what he had inside and why he was doing this.

He thought of the times that he got too caught up in his business, his goals and his agenda that he forgot why he was doing it at all. Karl brought his awareness back to the present moment, back to the footsteps in front of him. He contemplated the pulse of life happening all around him, and he felt the beating of his own heart, beating, he thought, in rhythm with all that was around him in this moment.

It was like the book that sat with the others on Karl's shelf. The shelf he gave thanks to nearly every day as he passed it. *Life is Tremendous,* by Charlie "Tremendous" Jones, the infinitely encouraging book about the persuasive power of enthusiasm. This book reminded Karl that the more involved and excited he was with his own goals, the more he would attract others into what he was doing. He knew that enthusiasm acts like a magnet and draws others who are like-minded into the circle of activity and interest. His greatest accomplishment came from this enthusiasm and here he was again drawing out that same fervor.

Zanzibar
CHAPTER 7

Listen TO YOUR SHOWER VOICE

Day 4
Start: Barranco Camp, 13,070 feet
Terrain: Rocky Desert
Duration: 6 hours
End: Karanga Camp, 13,255 feet:

Now, over 13,000 feet. The highest ground that Karl ever stood upon. Every bit of rise, every inch of incline was arduous to the point of pain. The cold weather clothes were in effect and sleeping without any warmth from the sun was agonizingly freezing when they could finally find a bunk to hide in. Day 4 was a hustle up the Barranco Wall leading to outstanding landscape views.

Soon, there would be no sleep in the night and just the journey to the summit to catch the sunrise. His body was weakened, but his mind and drive kept him going. The people, the memories, the life he's led all kept him going.

Karl came a long way from the days he worked into oblivion staring at a computer screen with weary eyes. Still, Karl couldn't help but visualize for the sake of sanity the feeling of warmth in an office. He took himself right back there just to remember the feeling. Ah, the comfort of a chair.

He remembered those days vividly. His imagination was so active and so real, it was as if he could relive a day all over again. He recalled one day in particular.

It had been another long day at work, and he was ready to leave. He agreed to meet his friend Richard Barrier at the gym to play racquetball after work, and he was excited at the prospect of getting some exercise. He needed it. As he drove the few miles through rush-hour traffic, he continued to think about work, but felt like he couldn't get any traction on the problems. His mind was like a pair of flat-soled shoes that just kept slipping on the steep incline of the mountainous challenges he faced toward building and saving his own business. As he approached the gym, he decided to stop thinking about work, and let go of his worries for at least a short while.

Richard was waiting for him in the lobby. They greeted each other, changed into their gym clothes, and entered the enclosed space of the racquetball court. Once inside, he was comforted by the compression of sound and space, and felt like he could focus his mind clearly on the game. He felt more centered than he had been all day, and played with an intensity of determination he wished he felt more often at work. After a half hour of playing in virtual silence, except for commenting on the progression of the game, Richard struck up the conversation, asking Karl how things had been going lately.

"Actually," he said, "I feel so good right now, I don't even want to think about how things are at work."

"I know what you mean," retorted Richard.

"Because there's so much going on," he continued, "that it feels chaotic just walking in the door. As soon as I sit down at my desk, I'm pummeled by a torrential onslaught of responsibilities. And I asked for this!"

"It's very challenging to remain connected with your own sense of self when you're surrounded with so much going on around you," Richard agreed.

"Tell me about it!" he shouted. "So many decisions to make, contracts to follow up on, questions to answer; sometimes I think if I didn't show up everything would completely fall apart." Karl paused to strike the ball with his racquet. "But maybe it's all in my head. Maybe, somehow I'm bringing my own chaotic mind to work, and that's what is stressing me out."

"You've got a good point there, Karl," Richard responded. "It's important to find a way to center your mind, to have a place you can go to tune into your creative thinking, and prepare yourself for work."

"Playing ball like this," he said with a gasp as he lunged for the ball, "feels pretty good for my body and my mind."

"Sure it is." Richard let the ball whizz by him and bounce back before hitting it against the far wall. "The same way you are conditioning your body for health right now, you can also condition your mind for success."

He stood poised to hit the ball, waiting for Richard to serve. "Exercise definitely clears the mind and aligns it with the body. But it's also important to know where you have your best thoughts, to know where and when you have the most brilliant thinking. For me it's the shower."

"Really?" Karl replied with a laugh. "I relax so much in the shower that I don't think much at all. As a matter of fact, I try not to think in the shower."

"Well then we've narrowed down the options for you, Karl. I didn't say all people do their best thinking in the shower. I just know that I do. I think it's a waste to let the great ideas I have in the shower go down the drain with all the water." Richard served the ball, then said, "You've got to determine where and when you do your best thinking, and utilize that to build upon your success in life."

"Hmm," he pondered. "I'll have to consider that. I'm thinking so much of the time, I really just want a place to go where I can let go of all my thoughts."

"That's important too," Richard agreed. "You've got to clear the clutter out of your mind before you can begin thinking creatively."

After hearing this Karl thought about a secluded place in the woods where he often walked to be alone and enjoy the solace of nature. He understood that exercise cleared his mind, but he needed to go the extra step and find a way to cultivate the creative thinking necessary to make his business succeed.

"You've given me an interesting direction for a new experiment," he told Richard. "I think I want to wrap up the game and go somewhere I might be able to find my own brilliant thoughts."

"Sure thing." Richard smiled. "I'm glad to have helped. And I think I'm about ready for a shower!"

Karl laughed and launched the final serve of the game. After playing out the point and conceding the game to Richard, he went into the locker room, changed back into his day clothes, and said goodbye to his friend. He walked to his car and drove to a place where he could set out on foot to his secret spot in the woods.

Karl looked around at Kilimanjaro. It was a different place but it was still one of magnificent nature.

His thinking was actually different in that spot. With his working woes at a distance, he was able to see beyond them and to think on a much grander scale. He saw the goals of his life and his business more clearly, and envisioned the path to travel towards them. He also realized that his goals and the journey toward them were not completely different, and that enjoying the journey was as vital a part of the whole process as was arriving at the goals.

Listen to Your Shower Voice

He smiled as he wrote it.

Karl committed then to practicing this principle more fully in his day-to-day work life. This climb, the nature surrounding him, while enduring, allowed him to find that place inside him again.

Zanzibar
CHAPTER 8

Bathroom BREAK

Day 5
Start: Karanga Camp
Duration: short 4 hour hike today.
End: Barafu, 15,360 feet.
Extra: Team will go to bed for the day at 4 p.m. to prepare for the summit push.

Karl felt a grumble in his stomach as he got up to stretch. Though his body demanded food, his mind was completely uninterested.

"I need a bathroom break!" Joyce yelled out. The group's pace had slowed to rests between every twenty steps. The rests were getting closer and closer in between the steps.

The wait for Joyce ended up being longer because the married couple on the trip had a setback. Jan suffered a bout of dysentery and became even more dehydrated than she already was.

Karl took every moment that they weren't climbing and sat down while the bathroom break continued. Those two words took him right back to Nana.

Bathroom Break

Between multiple meetings, heated discussions with other colleagues, and pressures building to make critical decisions regarding the future goals and strategies of his organization, Karl was emotionally exhausted. He felt the distinct urge to somehow escape the entire situation. Driving home that night, he decided to take a roundabout route where he could enjoy some natural scenery and let his mind clear. It was twilight, and purplish hues radiated through leafless trees, as the sky became soft and smooth as skin, and clouds stretched like silk through the transformation of colors.

He was so enchanted by the beauty of the world that he parked his car, and walked through an open, grassy park. As his work mind cleared and became filled with the inspiring scene of nature, he wondered why his human life was so often tainted with discouragement and turmoil.

Returning to his car, he opened the door and saw that he had a voicemail on his cell phone. His father called and invited him to have dinner with him and a couple who his father had known for some time. He quickly returned his phone call and accepted the invitation. It would be good, he thought, to spend some time with other people, instead of focusing on his own problems.

At the restaurant, his father introduced him to his friends Nana and her husband Lee Hinsley. As they enjoyed a steaming bowl of tomato bisque soup, Nana talked about exciting business plans that she and her husband had recently struck with another company. Karl listened with interest until Nana asked him about his own business which she knew about from his father. He was sure he frowned briefly, and said he was a bit hung-up in that area of his life. "I'd really rather not talk about it. This dinner is so nice; I don't want to give any of you indigestion with my sad story."

Nana laughed and egged him on, saying, "There's nothing you could tell me that my husband and I haven't been through yet. We know how hard it is to succeed in the world of business." She paused, then said, "But first you need to succeed in your own personal life; that's truly the hardest thing."

Karl smiled awkwardly and nodded, saying, "Yes, I believe you're right. So my life is really in more of a shambles than I thought!"

Nana laughed again, and consoled him, saying, "Let me tell you something about my own past. My husband and I weren't always so successful in our business, or personal life. Years ago we reached a point where things were so bad that all we could do was to hold onto the redeeming aspects of our relationship and our business. We learned then that the positive things we were doing had the power to help us rise above the murky swamps into which we had fallen. It sounds like you're face down in the swamp right now, Karl, but there's no reason you can't work your way out of it."

"You've got my attention," he sputtered over his soup. "Please, tell me how you two turned things around."

"Well," Nana started, "we decided to focus on the vision we had for our lives and our business, regardless of the hardships we faced. We copied quotes that expressed our values and ideals, as well as pictures that inspired us and related to our dreams. Then, Karl, you might find this unusual, but we taped them all on the wall in the bathroom at our workplace."

At this, everyone at the table let out a sudden spurt of laughter, while Nana smiled at Lee.

Taking over the story for a moment, Lee claimed, "That way, we knew all our employees would reflect on our beliefs and intentions. Because everyone has to go to the bathroom, right?"

He laughed again, and asked them about the results of such an uncanny experiment.

"Things gradually improved," said Nana. "Then one day, quite recently actually, an interesting thing happened."

"What's that?" he asked. He was thoroughly interested.

"Well," Nana continued, "one day a main competitor from a giant corporation came to meet with us. Midway through our meeting he took a bathroom break and didn't come back for an entire hour. When he did, he told us he was looking to buy a company, but wanted to purchase one that had the same vision and integrity as his own. According to our bathroom wall, he said we were the one. One day we may be interested in buying your company for twenty-five million dollars!"

"Wow!" Karl yelled. "That's great."

"Yes," agreed Nana. "It's such a wonderful feeling to know that the value we placed and instilled in the company is seen by others. We set our intentions, opened up the possibility of success, and opportunity presented itself." She paused, as if reflecting upon something. Then she said, "It seems like such a difficult thing, but once we were aligned with our true sense of purpose, everything else unfolded.

"By recognizing what we really wanted and holding ourselves accountable for our visions, we began living lives of honesty and integrity. We realized we had to be completely true to ourselves, to work every day to create what we wanted. In that way, we kept our word to our employees of ultimate success in our business. That's how we began to live lives of personal affirmation."

"Thanks for sharing your story with me," Karl said to Nana and Lee. "It seems that this delicious soup was the appetizer to a much more fulfilling meal, your incredible words of wisdom."

Karl thanked his dad for inviting him out to dinner, and left the restaurant, realizing that people can be affected in any way and at any time. The next day at work, he began to apply the same principle that Nana and Lee had used in their workplace bathroom. He constructed a creative space in the lunchroom at his organization where he put up the words and images that reflected the goals and visions he held for his company. He invited others to contribute to his visionary collage, and it soon became a collective space of creative collaboration where everyone shared their visions and dreams.

Liz even liked it so much that she created the same space in their home office. Karl exhaled, thinking about Liz and their home and how the happy times shined so strongly now after the rough times. As soon as he got a bit of mental fuel within him, Jan and Nathan were ready to go. The hikers were in as good as condition as they could be and so the climb continued.

Zanzibar
CHAPTER 9

Replenish THE DEFICIENCIES

Day 6
Part I: Summit
Start: Barafu Camp, 15,360 feet
Duration: 7.5 hours – midnight to 7:30 a.m.
End: Summit, 19,340 feet:

Karl heard the echoes of the couple's quivering groans through the night and way into the early morning hours. The day was intense as the terrain had gotten steeper and steeper on the way up to their camp. It was a difficult night and a more discouraging early morning. They all had so much clothing on now that it was hard to discern whether it was the steep climb that prevented them from moving any faster or the immobility of the clothing.

Some were puking along the way and some needed a bulk of enticement for each step. They were zigzagging with two steps moving them forward and one step moving them back. They climbed, they rested and they hydrated. This process left no room for alterations.

The steeper they went, the colder it got. The rest stops were increasing as the steps in between minimized, but the roof of Africa was still nearing. The feeling of separateness from everything else in the world was putting lessons Karl already learned into even deeper, more penetrating perspective. It was almost like experiencing an epiphany each time a memory was triggered and relived.

Once upon a time, Karl never would have dreamed to exert himself so much. He never would have chosen to conquer something so great. His habits were to keep doing the same things and if it felt uncomfortable, then he should stop. So, nothing changed. But here he was and everything had changed.

The group would be awoken near midnight to continue the course to the top where they would be welcomed and rewarded with the summit sunrise. It wasn't too difficult for Karl and the others to rest this time. Their bodies were screaming for it. But, they knew when it was time to hike through the night, they wouldn't be done screaming.

Eleven thirty at night marked the wake up call. Another layer of clothing was put on as the porters instructed. It was dark, cold and most of the group's mouths were frosted and everyone's feet were jolting.

Six hours of hiking and the sunrise neared. The path narrowed. To look down the snow-sided crater could easily set someone with equilibrium challenges into complete tragedy. Walking sticks were being used with the minimal energy that was left. The energy of the group was quite a distance from even a brisk walk by one healthy person.

Glaciers circled the summit and signs were posted warning climbers to stop if their bodies were too weak. But, everyone pressed on until the sun began to rise.

At first there was silence and then quiet tears followed by shouts of joy. Karl witnessed it all. His breath was completely taken away by the sheer beauty, let alone the exhaustion. He did it. He made it to the top.

The hikers embraced each other. Some convulsed with exhilarating tears. Some simply stood at the top with accomplishment and wonder.

Karl took in the scene. He embraced the moment, still feeling the deficiencies his body was experiencing. And at the peak of his climb, while watching Joyce take photos of the moment, his thoughts turned to Gerri Kier.

Replenish the Deficiencies

He had seen Gerri's photographs at the community art center a few times before meeting her. Her photographs had impressed him with their unusual qualities of perspective, which told him something about her intense curiosity. It was at the monthly art night event that they finally met, as she stood by her photographs, talking with someone who was interested in a particular print. He waited until she was finished with the person, then approached her and introduced himself as an appreciator of her photographs. Gerri thanked him, then said that, after over twenty years of full-time endeavor, she was no longer pursuing photography as a profession. He grimaced in displeasure and asked her why.

Gerri did not mirror his displeasure but maintained a highly spirited composure, and said, "About eight years ago I developed an ailment of tremors in my hand which has prevented me from being able to take clear shots." She smiled and laughed as if it were some kind of entertaining cosmic joke that a professional photographer should lose their ability to hold their camera steady. "But even though I've had to stop practicing photography, new opportunities have opened for me which have helped me to learn more about my purpose in life."

Karl looked at her in puzzlement as she continued.

"Since then I began to study natural health and became a digestive enzyme specialist. It's all quite fascinating to me how things happen unexpectedly. I've discovered that when one door closes, another door opens. Although I never would have consciously chosen to take this new path, it's benefited me in ways I couldn't have imagined before I was redirected by unforeseen events to change direction in my life and career."

He told her he respected her capacity to see the redeeming aspects of events that appear to be catastrophic in the moment. Although inwardly he still felt saddened that she could no longer pursue her love of photography. That was until she told him what happened next.

"The wonderful thing is, as I learned about healing through nutritional supplements, the body can heal itself when it is fed what it is lacking. So I'm able to pursue photography, but now that I've learned about natural healing I've chosen to continue in this direction by building a natural health and wellness emporium. It's all very new and exciting! For some reason life gave me a tremendous gift by first taking something valuable away. I think because I accepted what happened, and took it in stride without resisting the change too much, I eventually got back what I valued so much."

The idea of accepting such a painful loss without fighting it seemed, at the time, impossible for Karl. He told this to Gerri. But he also told her how amazing it was that not only did she inadvertently heal her debilitating condition through proper nutrition; she also discovered a new professional path that held immense interest for her.

"I knew from your photographs that you were a very interesting and talented person, but I never fathomed that you were so wise!" he said to her.

Gerri looked a bit embarrassed and said it wasn't that she was wise, but that she had just been able to accept a difficult situation and follow the tracks in the sand of her life to the next stage.

Karl felt so moved by Gerri's story that he kept in touch over the years. After learning that she participated in mountain climbs where she raised money for countries in need of education, he became even more interested in manifesting his own dream to climb Kilimanjaro.

In subsequent meetings with Gerri over coffee and scones, she shared her philosophy about the importance of recognizing our deficiencies, personally, emotionally, as well as in business. She taught him to look at where he is lacking and replenish himself with what he needs, to be aware of his weaknesses, but focus on his strengths and emphasize the possibility in any situation. This helped him to identify his own health deficiencies in preparing to climb Kilimanjaro, so that he could condition himself properly and operate from an optimal place.

He thought back on how it had been so vital for him to become finely attuned to his overall health, and to condition himself not only physically, but also mentally and emotionally for the most aspiring climb of his life so far. Without Gerri's guidance he might have never developed such a keen awareness and ability to replenish his deficiencies with strengths.

Karl then thought more about how the preparation to climb Kilimanjaro had also prepared him to take his business to new heights. Climbing Kilimanjaro, in retrospect, had served as a metaphor for taking his life and his business to the optimal place he had to learn to cultivate in order to climb the mountain. In the world of business, life is full of many challenges, not all as imposing as Kilimanjaro; but having accomplished one previously insurmountable goal energized Karl to descend the mountain and return to his life.

Because his business was his livelihood, Karl reflected, it was a central feature of his life, which he needed to develop just as fully as his personal relationships. Thinking about his business as a central expression of his life purpose, Karl envisioned the exciting new things he could do, and the incredible new places he could take his business in the future. Reflecting this, the possibilities astounded him. Observing the other hikers, sharing their reactions to the summit and every piece of rock, snow and dirt that surrounded him, he felt inspired. Every moment, every challenge, every person, every book was instrumental in his life and throughout this journey they were like bubbles rising from the stream reminding him of their significance. Somehow, he wanted everyone to experience what he was feeling. But how?

Zanzibar
CHAPTER 10

Life IS A BOOMERANG

Day 6
Part II: Descend from roof of Africa
Start: Summit, 19,340 feet
Duration: 5 hours
End: Mweka Camp, 10,500 feet:

It doesn't take long to figure out that you don't hang out at 19,000 feet. As impressive as the summit was and the feelings everyone had over their achieved dreams, the broiled faces and chapped lips were reminders that what goes up must come down.

Whatever materials they read, they all received the message that the descent would be a relief. While it was easier, the muscles used to go down were far different from those used to ascend. But, just as they were out of tune going up, they remained out of tune going down. Karl felt like Bambi as he wavered on the steep parts.

"So what'd you think?" Her name was Michele Massion and she didn't speak much during the climb. Not that she wasn't friendly, she was just focused. Outside of minor conversation amidst the group, Michele was one of the observers of the group taking in every bit of experience.

"Do you want the truth?" Karl asked.

"I'm only good with truth. Don't care for the BS." She was direct.

"It was probably the most frightening, borderline horrendous, voluntary activity I have ever chosen to do. I'm wondering why anyone would pay to do this and at the same time, I've never felt better. You?"

"I'm just going to ditto you because that would be much easier."

When Michele looked at Karl to finish her words, something was familiar.

"Wait a minute. Are you..."

"It's me."

"Karl. I'm Karl Patrick from ..."

"Karl Patrick from the National CEO Conference."

"Do you remember me?"

"I noticed you from the profile pictures before we even boarded the flight. I was wondering how long it would take for you to remember me."

"Wow, I apologize. You look..." He searched for the right words. "Different?"

She laughed. "No, I'm still the same. Not much has changed. Except I look a lot better with a shower, some makeup and a little less padded clothing."

"Wow. I've been so wrapped up in my fear of this thing that I--"

"Karl, it's all right. It's kind of neat actually."

"How could I not recognize someone who greatly impacted my life?"

"Who? Me?"

"Heck, yeah!"

Karl had met Michele at a national business conference where they were designated to sit at the same table in a small group. Though she had only been involved in her trade for about five years, she had become quite successful, and was in the top two percent of her sales force. At the time, Karl had been struggling with his business and shared some of the challenges he'd been facing with Michele who became very interested in giving him feedback based on her own experiences.

"I totally get your concerns, Karl," Michele responded, "and I think we all have them. But you can't let yourself get too caught up in the monetary results of your business.

Not yet. It seems you're so focused on succeeding economically that you've lost touch with the truer meaning of success, which is to be had in the actual dealings of your business itself." She paused, then said, "You've lost your perspective. To quote an old saying, 'You can't see the forest for the trees.'"

In most instances, he probably would've been taken aback, felt a bit insulted and made some excuses in response to what Michele said. But the way she spoke conveyed that she truly understood where he was with his business, and was genuinely concerned for his well-being.

"Hmmm," he replied. "I'd love to tell you that you're wrong, but I think you're dead on with what you said. I've been so anxious about failure lately, that I haven't been able to enjoy my work much at all."

"I'll tell you a little secret," Michele smiled as she spoke. "If you put your attention and your energy into what you're doing at work, and into all your interactions with your clients, you will have much better results. Focus on the job itself, throw yourself fully into the process, and the results will come. But you know what? When you do this, the monetary results won't be nearly as important to you because your true reward is in the work you do. You'll find out that making a real difference in someone's life is worth much more than making lots of money. True success is being loved and respected by those around you, and being able to give to people who are appreciative."

Although he respected what Michele said, the voice in his head kept coming back to the bottom line of business expenditures that had to be met month after month. "That makes a lot of sense," he told Michele. "But if I don't earn enough, I may not be able to keep the business afloat."

"That's true," Michele agreed. "But if you don't enjoy what you're doing, why would you want to continue doing it anyway?" At this, everyone at the table nodded. Strangely enough, they let Michele continue to duke it out with him without interruption, like two boxers in the ring.

"I want to enjoy what I'm doing. I did enjoy it in the beginning. But then the bills started coming in, and they flooded me with fear. Now I'm so concerned about falling too far into the red that I can't enjoy what I'm doing anymore."

Michele seemed intent on breaking through Karl's stubbornness, and quickly replied, "No matter what sum the transaction is, Karl, it all adds up. Life is a boomerang. In one way or another, whatever you put into your business, you get back out of it. In my business, ninety-nine percent of my clients are based on referral, so I treat every deal equally, no matter what. Focus on each transaction, on each client, and on each deal with equal attention and care. Eventually it will all come back to you."

At last he had nothing to say. Michele's words were succinct and poignant. Furthermore, he knew she was right. So he thanked her for her suggestions, and said he'd make his best efforts to put them into practice.

Karl refreshed Michele's memory as their breaths jumped in conversation with the downward climb.

"After that meeting, I realized that you were really just encouraging me to follow the path of my original vision. I had lost perspective, and you helped me to restore it. I realized that it takes time for any business to succeed, but that if I put enough into the pot, it would eventually add up to what I was seeking. I learned to stop worrying so much about the money, and to focus on the work at hand. And on manifesting the vision I had when I began my business. In essence, I realized that if I trust the process, the right thing will happen." He took a deep breath in after his spew.

"Really? You got all of that from me?"

"You felt so available and accessible to me. You taught me that those who are the most successful at what they do are also the most available and accessible to others. Consistent actions yield consistent results."

"And you didn't even recognize me?"

"Hell, I barely recognize myself right now."

They walked until the next rest period. Karl opened his journal for just a quick moment

Life is a Boomerang

He put down his pen, and sighed with appreciation for his encounter with Michele. Enjoying the sigh, he shut his eyes. In just seconds he was whisked into a deep nap that left him practically motionless, other than the small lung contractions visible from his belly.

When his eyes opened it was time to grab something to eat. His appetite was back as the air was more favorable and the conditions less extreme. He started to feel refreshed and sensed he was beginning to learn more about himself than he ever had. Climbing Kilimanjaro had inspired him with a new vision of his life in which he could finally see his path with a full 360 degrees of perspective. He was beginning to see how every degree of perspective, from the past through the present, and into the future, all interrelated perfectly with one another. Finally, his life was beginning to make sense. More clearly than ever, Karl knew where he came from, where he was now, and where he was going.

Zanzibar
CHAPTER 11

Pay IT BACKWARDS

Breathing was still an issue for Karl in the climb, but he knew he needed to work hard in order to get through this. It wasn't just about working hard though. It was about working smart. He learned this from this one woman he met in line, getting a bagel and coffee just weeks before his trip.

"Just the coffee and the bagel?" the barista asked Karl.

"That'll do me today." He was in a reflective mood, questioning himself.

"Ok, that's two fifty today, sir."

"And the coffee too?"

"Yes, I got that. But, you're drink's been taken care of."

Karl was confused. "Excuse me?"

"Yes, the lady ahead of you purchased your coffee."

"I don't understand. I don't know her."

"Well, she must like you." He was a young barista, probably in school.

"I wasn't paying attention. Is she still here? I'd like to thank her."

The young man looked around and squinted. "Um. Oh yeah, that's her. She just took a seat outside. The one reading a book."

Karl paid the man and took his bagel and coffee. "Great, thank you."

He grabbed a sugar and poured some cream in his coffee and went straight to the table the woman where the woman sat. She was reading a book and smiling.

"Pardon me. I hate to interrupt."

She looked up and broadened her grin.

"You bought my coffee."

"Oh. Lucky you!"

Now Karl was really taken aback. Did she not know that she bought his coffee? Was it intentional?

"Uh." He started to stutter. "Did you mean to do that?"

"I most certainly did." She looked him right in the eye and while she wasn't saying much, Karl couldn't help but feel connected to her.

"I'm sorry but I don't understand why."

She gestured to the empty seat at her table. "Would you like to sit? Enjoy the coffee?"

Karl accepted and sat down and began to spread butter on his bagel.

"I'm Kathy Curtis by the way."

Karl wiped the crumbs from his hand and offered it to her for a handshake. He appreciated her firm handshake. "Karl. Or maybe you knew that?"

"Hmm. No, it's not often I know the names of the people I buy drinks for."

A light bulb went off in Karl's head just then. "Ah, I think I understand now. So, you just like to buy coffee for random people?"

Kathy laughed, a very infectious one at that. "Well, the random part is right. I believe in random acts of paying it backwards."

"Really?"

"Sure. And my hope is that each person that takes notice and appreciates the gesture will do the same to the person behind them in line next time."

"Well, you can be certain I will." Karl continued, "So, can I ask why you do this?"

"Well, I've come to notice that it feels really good to have an impact on other people."

"Well, you definitely impacted me."

"I'm glad. Whether it's a little act here or there, I feel like I'm making a difference and if each person is affected by that then I feel that somehow we are all connecting and making a difference on a larger scale. Even further, we learn more when we get to interact with others. Like you. Here. Today."

"I've definitely learned something from you."

"Fantastic!"

"You're one of the most authentic people I've ever met, Kathy."

"Hey, authenticity is authority! Stay true to yourself and your authenticity will never be questioned."

Karl knew this to be true first hand. "You couldn't be more right. You know sometimes I question my own authenticity."

"Oh, we're the first to question ourselves, often times before anyone else can. But, if we don't feel authentic then we are most likely not in touch with who we really are."

"So, Kathy, how do you get past that?"

"Well, for me, whenever I feel in doubt of what I am doing, I look to the actions I am taking and focus on the impact they are making on others. I look at the things I am doing now that bring positive impacts and I put more attention on those and filter out those that aren't. To me that's working smart. It's not always easy. You have to work hard at it sometimes. But, better to work hard and smart then to work hard and be stuck."

Karl nodded. He had realizations of his own at that very moment.

"That includes self-doubting thoughts, Karl. Do those create a positive impact on you or others?"

It was as if she was reading his mind. "Ha! Absolutely not. You know I've been in business for many years now and that's something that can easily be forgotten. So many people I know, including myself get upset when we work so hard and don't see the results we want. We forget that we have to work smart too."

"And when you stay authentic, you can't help but work smart. You feel happier. You do nicer things and you don't have to think twice."

"Easy enough! I sure hope most of these people pay it backwards to get the chance to speak with you like I did."

"Well, not all of them. But, my hope is that they always do the right thing!"

After saying goodbye to Kathy that day, he refilled his coffee and bought the person behind him their drink of choice. Putting the focus on one nice gesture made him feel authentic and purposeful.

Karl took a swig of water as he brought his mind back to his descent from the ceiling of Africa. Even before this trip, just weeks before, he doubted what he was doing, why he was doing it and what impact it would have, not realizing that that in itself was hindering his authenticity.

Pay It Backwards

Zanzibar
CHAPTER 12

Greatest LIE EVER TOLD

As his breathing felt easier than it had in days, Karl noted the feeling of the oxygen exchange in his lungs and the moment he could feel the transition from easy breaths to difficult. He was grateful for this moment when it felt so fluid. He remembered the moment his thoughts changed from excitement and awe that he was finally climbing to the moment he was coaching himself with every step until the next rest stop. Was it his thoughts?

He thought of Wayne Dyers' book *Change Your Thoughts, Change Your Life,* and how, in one day, reading that book had a profound impact upon him. It was an exceedingly interesting book as it explored various translations and meanings of the ancient *Tao Te Ching* by Lao-tzu. Each essay in itself illuminating, while Dyers' critique and pontification aided immensely in applying the life lessons to modern times. It came at a time when Karl's thoughts were his own enemy. He learned how changing them would aid in developing his character and to broaden and deepen his personality.

But the moments of uncertainty and doubt would still come back. It was often enough on this climb. How should he be feeling? Was this normal? Did everyone else feel this way? Was he weak if he needed a rest? Was his faith in himself or higher being not strong enough? Would the ascent have been easier? Did he appreciate the summit as much as everyone else did?

He could hear others in conversation as he tried to halt the incoming barrage of nonproductive questions.

"Well, I can't lie on that one. That one was pretty brutal. If I didn't have to answer to me, I think I would have passed." She laughed and her laugh was infectious. Karl hadn't heard the laugh since before they embarked. It was obvious many of the hikers were feeling better. That laugh reminded him of Linda Rocco.

He was in his late twenties and it was just another ordinary day. At that point, he hadn't yet started his business, but had some inkling about what he wanted to do. However, he didn't yet quite believe that he could do it, and was still floundering with work that was just getting him by, waiting for something to snap him into gear.

But when he met Linda at the laundromat that afternoon, he was making sure not to mix his black pants in with the white shirts.

There he was, waiting for the spin cycle, reading an old science fiction book, and along she came looking elegant and energetic. He watched as she put her two loads of laundry into the machines, then, much to his surprise, she walked over next to him and sat down. There were plenty of other places to sit, but she decided to sit next to Karl.

"Hi," she said, extending her hand. "I'm Linda. What's your name?"

Somewhat startled by her forwardness, Karl was slow to respond. "Um, I'm Karl," he managed to get out. Then, speaking with trepidation in his voice, he said, "Nice … to … meet … you."

"So, what are you reading?" she asked in a lively and animated tone, her eyes radiating beams of light.

"Oh." He was so taken off guard, he had forgotten the book and had to look at it to remember, "This is *Dandelion Wine*, one of my favorites."

Linda looked delighted to have learned about his book, and quickly replied in a wondrous manner, "Really? What's it about?"

"Well," he began then paused, half-suspecting that someone was playing a trick on him. "I'll tell you what it's about if you tell me what's going on." For the first time, Linda looked a bit confused, so he said, "Why did you sit down right next to me and start talking with me? It's just that it's so unusual. I mean, we're virtual strangers, how can you even trust me?"

Linda looked a bit relieved and said, "I don't have to trust you Karl, I only have to trust myself and my own instincts about who is safe and who isn't. Come on now, you don't think many serial killers hang out reading science fiction books in laundromats planning their murderous conquests, do you?"

He laughed and said, "No, not really."

"Society and the media, even our parents and education, have trained us to think and behave in certain ways that aren't always good for us. They tell us what's okay and what isn't, what's safe and what's dangerous, as if their words of advice were some kind of social law. When I was younger, I totally fell for that. I was taught to be submissive and only do the things that other people told me I could do. But then I realized that following other people's rules isn't good for me, unless I happen to agree with them."

"Wow, you're a really deep thinker," he sputtered.

"Being bound by what others say is right never satisfied my soul, Karl. We have to choose the so-called laws that we live by, and if they don't make common sense, then they're really not very good laws, are they?"

"I guess they're not," he mumbled. "But I think I've been living by other people's rules, by other people's laws, as you say, for a long time."

"Eventually, I found that living like that, according to other people's rules, made me feel like the real me just wasn't good enough. So I decided to start making my own rules, and to live according to what made good sense to me. Eventually, I found the courage to take a stand, and to be committed to satisfying my own soul. Because this is my life, so why should someone else determine how I live it?"

Karl glanced over at the washing machine which had stopped spinning right when Linda finished her last thought. He felt both nervous and excited that she had shared so much of her life experience with him, and in such an unexpected fashion. It was like a brilliant firework display had suddenly gone off in his mind, and he wasn't sure what to say. "All I know is you're one of the bravest people I've ever met. And I'm sure glad you decided to talk with me like this."

"Just remember one thing," Linda said. "honor who you are! If you live your life the way other people expect you to, your life will be the greatest lie ever told. Because conformity isn't freedom. And everything that we think is real is just the made-up story of our culture." Linda looked serious for the first time, and said, "So, you've got to make up your own story, because it's the only one that's really yours."

His unexpected encounter with Linda at that time had provided the spark he needed. It was just enough to get focused on what he really wanted to do in life and to at least answer the question of what it was he wanted in life.

It was a good day. That was the day he experienced, in true form, motivation. Without worrying what others would think, his own thoughts quieted down and he was able to hear his real self.

Heading to a new campsite, Karl revisited that same lesson he learned from Linda and his readings, and became stronger than the nagging voice and trusted his true inner voice.

As the night drifted on and camp was set up, Karl decided to do a little exploring as the final dinner at the mountain was being prepared.

He looked around, but saw nothing. Perhaps nothing frolicked in such high altitude. Perhaps he didn't need to see anything at all, but just listen.

Zanzibar
CHAPTER 13

Life PRINT

In the final four hours of the hike back to the main gate Karl enjoyed the quiet. He kept envisioning the phone call to his wife, the days to follow in Zanzibar and how he wished she could be there with him on vacation. The feeling of appreciation and wanting all that he had was a thrill, no doubt inspired by the climb. He remembered the days when he used to tell himself, "Someday, I'll…" and how important it was that he was doing the things he set out to do and leaving his own life print.

Life Print

He wrote it down.

It was at one of those first turning points in his career when he reached a pivotal place that challenged him to step up and to come forward with a new and stronger sense of self, a self that didn't hide in the shadows, but was willing to lay it all out on the table, and to lay in on the line. He'd been playing it safe, and avoiding risks his whole career. He came to a point where he knew, if he was to grow, he needed to change, and he needed to leave behind small living, small thinking and his small ordinary sense of self. It was time to expand his business and start to focus on the larger corporations wanting to renovate their structures into sustainable buildings.

Luckily, that's when he met Eileen Schwartz. She was sharp and very talented at what she did. They'd come across each other in business for years, and though he knew of her by name, they hadn't really met until a fellow colleague introduced them. There was something in the way she spoke to him, with firmness in her voice, and a great clarity in her eyes, that let him know right off that she was on her game.

Eileen was a person who, just during the course of a conversation over lunch, made him feel ten times more important, intelligent and capable than he normally felt. Because she so easily identified with the greatness in herself, she immediately helped him to identify with his own. But she also pointed it out to him. "You know, Karl," she said, "I think you are the only person who can't see your greatness, because it's overwhelmingly obvious to the rest of us what a talented person you are. Not only do you orchestrate a team so efficiently, but the projects are done in the time you say they will be. That's a rarity in the construction business."

Karl felt embarrassed when she said this, but deep down inside his intuit was that she was right. "I've got to be honest, Eileen. I'm half excited and half scared to take on something so big."

"It's time to eliminate the option of failure, Karl."

"What?"

He wasn't sure what she meant, but he liked the sound of failure not being an option. She continued, "You know that part of you that gets excited? The part of you that drives you and wants to do bigger and better things?"

"Um, yeah." He was anxious to see where she was going with this.

"Live from that. Operate from that place, Karl."

He was getting it.

She said, "The place where you had that burning passion to start your own business in the first place? That's how you did it. You were operating from your own place of greatness. Right there, inside you. It's still there, you just lose touch with it every now and then and that's when the fear comes in. That's when you leave it to 'someday' instead of today!"

Karl laughed as he experienced the epiphany he needed to move forward with his goals.

"There it is," Eileen smiled as she saw Karl light up. "That's where you want to be. You have everything you need right inside of you and you just showed it to me and to yourself. That's where the vision comes. Once you can connect with that, you can achieve anything."

He knew that he needed to bring forth a greater self-respect and self-esteem in order to make his business grow. He knew he needed to recognize it within himself before anyone else would share the same confidence. One of Eileen's gifts was being able to bring out in people what they didn't see in themselves. She was like a lighthouse, shining rays of light into other people's darkness—which is simply a way of saying that she helped other people to see what they were not aware of in themselves. Her mission was to illuminate people's souls to the degree that she was able, by reflecting back to them the goodness she saw inside them. By operating from the greatness within, there is an illumination of the soul and that's when a life print is left in this world that is passed on. The world is left a little bit better.

While he tended to focus on his weaknesses at times of potential and big changes, Eileen encouraged him to work with his strengths, and to stay focused on his capabilities and his own potential. "Don't let your weaknesses get you down, Karl," she would tell him. "We all have weaknesses, and we all have strengths. When we focus on the weaknesses, we lose touch with what's inside and we start to search outside, forgetting that everything we need is right inside of us. If you focus on your strengths and you operate from that feeling of knowing the success, it will lead you. Eventually your weak areas will get stronger by default."

By encouraging him to look at what he was really good at, and to make these qualities even better, Eileen helped Karl develop his strengths and move forward in the areas he could. As if she were perfectly ordained to come into his life precisely when she did, her encouragement enabled him to become the bolder, more enterprising businessman he needed to become. In effect, she helped him discover the next stage in his human development, one in which he really deeply began to trust and believe in himself. It was then that he began to realize what leaving a life print meant.

"Don't wait for tomorrow to come," Eileen admonished him. "Someday may never be. No more 'someday, I'll do this,' or 'tomorrow I'll make that change.' Make it happen now. The moment you can do something, you should do it. Don't let the moment pass. Let that illumination and greatness serve you and everyone else. That impression will be long lasting and will affect people time and time again."

Eileen was right. He had spent a lot of his life dreaming about someday, and had avoided taking action to really manifest those dreams. She showed him, through the example of her own life, that taking chances, trusting the moment, and acting on inspiration are all part of owning his greatness, and his potential. She taught him to realize his unlimited potential and to connect with his own vision. So often, he put his visions to the side because they didn't match what others taught him to believe. For Karl it was like this intense cleanse to get rid of the things in his life that were not supporting his greatness and to refuel and embrace himself with those who could see it and believe in it as much as he did. Eileen's life print left a great impression on Karl to not let dreams slip away, but to bring them into reality by believing in his own life print.

Zanzibar Chapter 14

Two CHOICES

Karl was feeling so strong and capable, successful in the eyes of the world and in the inner reckoning with his own soul as he marched his final day down the mountain. But it wasn't always like this. He didn't always feel so strong and successful. In the early days of developing his business, he ran into many problems, and experienced many set-backs and failures. In retrospect, his failures were actually opportunities to grow, to learn, and to find the right way of proceeding. Though he felt severely traumatized by any perceived failure to achieve his business goals back then, he could see so much more clearly how the failures were necessary challenges for his life to be made into something meaningful. Like the knife upon the wood by which the sculptor carves an image, so life put the same kind of pressures upon Karl, eventually creating something cohesive and satisfying.

He didn't learn this lesson completely alone. He recalled his good friend, Tish Taylor, who helped him navigate through the anguish of business failures, and to see them as something potentially worthy or helpful.

Two Choices

Tish was of such enormous support in his early years. In fact, she would have been incredible to have on this climb. She told Karl often how the only true failure is the failure to not even try. Because everyone tends to view failure as a sign of weakness, she pointed out that it is actually a process that makes us stronger, because it takes strength to live through a failure and to keep going.

"If success comes easy, what is its worth?" she would ask Karl. "The person who always succeeds eventually becomes weak, because, if they always succeed, they're probably not setting their goals very high. Your failures are like little victories, because they show you where you stand with life, and they bring forth the potential that lives inside you. Therefore, Karl, you should celebrate your failures!"

Karl laughed and felt strangely ridiculous at having complained when Tish greeted his failures by uncorking a bottle of wine as if to augment the celebration. But her actions were the sign of a deeper trust in life, a reliance on some principle at work that was larger than his own little ego. Over time, she taught him to take his knocks in stride, and to understand that life was continually trying to throw us off balance, but that taking the knocks kept us alert and ready for action.

Karl didn't really understand her counsel at first, but gradually, after enough failures, he saw that her beliefs stood for something. One day over lunch Tish told Karl how she came to feel this way.

"Before getting the position I am in now, I went through a very confusing and frustrating experience."

At the time Karl thought he knew Tish well enough to know if she had gone through something like this and was curious to what could have happened.

"Once upon a time I was ranked number three in my company."

"I remember that, I think," Karl contributed.

"Well, what you might not have known was that I was fired."

"What? How? I remember you stopped working for them, but I guess I didn't know you well enough to know what really happened. Wow. I always wondered what happened. I mean it was your best year, right?"

"Right. So, you can imagine how I felt being let go after being the top third producer in a company that was all new to me."

"What happened?"

"The frustrating part was that for the longest time, I didn't know what happened. I sought out every answer I could find. I went to human resources. I consulted with my clients. And all I got were rave reviews on my performance. It just didn't make sense."

"So, what did you do?"

"I had to let it go, Karl. It was eating me up inside. I knew that I could just stay frustrated or I could move on and take the things that did make sense and use that."

"And what was that?" Karl was intrigued.

"My clientele and doing my best. See, when I was a kid I got hundreds of rejections and to be honest they didn't mean anything to me. But, if I got just a 'maybe', I ran with it. I needed to go back to that kid and realize that the negative wasn't going to stop me. I knew that doing my best was serving my clients and that was all the fire I needed to move forward."

"I have to be honest with you, Tish. I would still be frustrated if I were you."

"Look, there are times when your failures can be empowering because they force you to re-group, to re-focus, and to strive harder with more effort toward your goals. Along with the virtue of being humble, my failures also showed me the value of success. I learned that if I always succeeded, I might stop trying so hard, and might not care so much about things. Life is a series of small decisions that lead us to the next adventure," Tish told Karl. "Embracing the circumstances from these decisions and learning from the failures allows us to continue on with enthusiasm. Failure is the celebratory proof of taking action!" In a sense, Tish didn't really believe in the concept of failure. As long as people put effort into what they were doing, they couldn't really fail. They would only learn more about themselves and what they were doing.

"For me, it comes down to this, Karl." She put out two fingers. "I believe in two choices. Either dwell on what didn't go right, or accept the lessons, learn from them and move forward."

It seemed so simple for Karl. Accepting failure was the hardest part, because he was taught to always win and to only take pride in winning. But failure brings a gift worth taking.

"Did you ever find out what happened, Tish?"

"I did. Fortunately, there was a new high executive. He didn't want any woman to overpower him."

"Fortunately?"

"Well, yeah. If he hadn't let me go, I wouldn't be where I am now."

"Ah, the two choices."

Tish raised her eyebrows with pride.

In the past, Karl's failures seemed to come with waves of shame, saturating him with heaviness, and temporarily paralyzing his creative spirit. Through Tish's encouraging words, he learned to forgive himself, and to keep going. True success, she showed him, was having the enduring commitment to visions and goals to keep pursuing them, even in the face of the greatest challenge. Karl appreciated very clearly how true her words were. He knows the success of having a relentless persistence and dedication, of not giving up or giving in, but believing in himself and striving towards his goals every day. While the worries and qualms will roll in from time to time, Karl was finding that instead of dwelling on them, he could instead accept them as part of life's ride. For every time the waves came in, a new perspective was revealed.

Zanzibar

CHAPTER 15

Touching TORCHES

Day 7
Start: Mweka Camp, 10,500 feet
Duration: 5 hours
End: Machame Gate, home!

He saw the Machame Gate and cars waiting just ahead. So many times, he wished for the warmth of a car, a city light or just moist lips. And there he was with a taste of melancholy his journey was coming to an end.

Karl and the group reached the gate at which they began and it came with dancing, singing and praise of the porters and each hiker's success. They looked tired, but filled with light. Their smiles told a different story and Karl wondered if his did too.

Looking over to where they first began, he spotted a new group awaiting their start. He watched them and sent them a silent touch of the torch with thanks to Luba Rusyn.

Touching Torches

She had great hair, penetrating eyes, and a face that glowed with radiance. As she spoke, she seemed to feel every word with her entire body, as if every part of her agreed with what she was saying and emanated a harmonic resonance. Karl knew it seemed odd, but if there were any modern day prophets, he was sure she might be among them. Something about the passion and sincerity in her words flowed out with such a calming urgency.

They began with small talk, such as where they were going and whom they were visiting. But after awhile the conversation grew deeper. She asked Karl if he ever thought about the meaning of his life, about why he was alive now, and what he came here to do in this lifetime. When he looked at her with some suspicion, she smiled. She said that people in general didn't like to think that maybe there was an intelligent plan behind life, or behind their own individual lives, but that she liked to think there was. She said this helped her to get more involved in her life and to feel more intrinsically connected with what she was doing, as if somehow, on some level, she was indeed creating her own reality.

Karl had to admit that while a part of him thought she was a bit crazy, a deeper part of him felt awakened and enlivened by her commentary. It was as if she was speaking about something he had known all along, but that had to come through her for him to be able to hear or appreciate it.

Meeting her was a very strange experience for Karl, because she seemed to be connected with something that he only had glimpses of, some kind of energy or greater awareness. The kind of thing that people refer to when they talk about angels or spirits. The kind of thing that, quite frankly, tended to make him uncomfortable.

When they met, Luba had talked about fire as a symbol of life, and about the torch as a beautiful representation of strength and passion. She had made the metaphor of the flames of the torch being like the creative, spiritual energy of life, which people pass on to one another. She had marveled at how, from torch to torch, the fire of knowledge, awareness and life energy was ignited and then passed on. She felt it was her mission to pass on her own life energy to others, to ignite their spirits and minds with the inspiration she carried.

"It's a continuous force, creating endless moments of explosive power from one conscious connection," she had told Karl. "By lighting the torch for others, we maintain the power of ignition, and the power to co-create a reality. We open the doors for others so that they, too, can experience transformation, new opportunities and growth. That's the power of healing; it makes you and whoever you've touched more whole."

Luba was specific about how she thought this happened. She laid out her plan to Karl in clear and simple terms. "There are just three steps to your starting your own ignition, Karl. First, you must have the torch of desire to connect with others. Second, you must have the inner fire and willingness to reach out and ask for help. Third, once you have been ignited, you must touch another torch and light the flame for another." She smiled, then said, "That's all it takes! Desire, willingness, and action."

Karl did most of the listening that day, because he had the most to learn from the conversation. Luba was very different from most other people he had met, and he enjoyed the opportunity to learn about life from her perspective. Though they never spoke again, her message stuck with him and affected how he thought and acted in the world. She told him that our allies help us to move forward, so it's important to identify who they are. And that creating the impetus for continuous ignition leads to a powerful alliance of human spirits in which a profound sense of interconnection and relatedness takes over.

Karl felt that interconnection happening at the end of his climb.

He heard the gathering crowd gaining momentum at the gate. He pulled off his backpack and stretched again. As he watched the new strangers, he opened his eyes a bit wider, smiled, and extended his both his heart and his mind, preparing to ignite new torches.

Zanzibar
CHAPTER 16

Personal ENVELOPMENT

White sand, turquoise water, and ships sailing by the most striking waters on earth. Known as the spice island by many, the beauty can be best described as nothing short of paradise. Karl Patrick sat off the coast of Zanzibar as natives walked proudly through the village. As a man who just climbed Mount Kilimanjaro, Karl appreciated the rest. He watched as an eager vendor rushed to his side to sell native trinkets and ointments that were guaranteed to bring good luck and cure his receding hairline. He couldn't help but give his attention.

The sounds of the waves were present, lapping up and retreating over again as they washed up against the shoreline. The longer he sat, the more the big calm settled in.

The big calm was something he had come to view as a tuning in process of cracking the surfaces so that the sounds of the proverbial ocean underneath the waves were heard. Karl found sheer awareness in the moment. It didn't take strenuous effort to gain this awareness; rather, it was arrived at with attention.

At first sight one might get the impression that this small seaside town was living a life of poverty, when in fact to Karl, they may be the most abundant civilization today. It was quite a bustling city compared to his last days.

Winding his way toward the local sands, he saw the fisherman divide the daily catch on shore. From hand-carved canoes, these sun baked farmers of the sea pulled huge nets from right below the surface in expectation of a bountiful harvest.

Karl wasn't used to this slow-paced lifestyle. When they said breakfast was served from seven to eleven, it simply meant you order your meal at seven in hopes to have it in hand by eleven. It seemed to be the way of the land around these parts and was most evident by the swiftness of the handcrafted schooners as they slid across the tide.

Karl spread his toes in the sand and sighted the newly crafted cabana that his exhausted body had been craving. He left a message for his wife, whom he was sure to be awaiting his call. But, she was probably sleeping or busy with Jake.

Sitting on this cliff, looking toward the mountain he recently climbed, Karl was inspired with a thirst for experiences which would enable him to discover new aspects of the world, but more importantly, new dimensions and farther reaches of his own inner world. This perspective was somewhat new to him. The climb up Kilimanjaro showed him another side of reality, perhaps it was the inner side, the side most closely connected to himself.

These realizations reminded him of someone he met one weekend last spring at Lake Gresham, where he had gone to escape the city for a while and enjoy a bit of relaxation.

Personal Envelopment

Clarissa Burt was energetic and smart. She was excelling in every area of her career, and very interested in ideas about self-discovery and healing. Having had success in media and being an expert in the field, she grew to have an extreme devotion to helping women.

They sat on the dock for an entire afternoon talking, and he remembered her words well, because everything she said was so convincing. "For so long," she told him,

"I've been trained by the world around me, especially by the media of television and advertising, to look good. I've been taught that looking good is more important than anything else. But the media tells me nearly nothing about the value of my inner experiences."

Clarissa felt that this was a tragedy and responsible for much unnecessary suffering in our society. Karl agreed with her, and told her so.

"The media does a fabulous job of placing extreme importance on our external appearances," she continued. "But, what might be a beautiful façade could conceal an unsightly battle on the inside. Yet, for many, it looks to be an easier fix to create the facade than to end the battle of slaying the inner demons." She spoke with a confidence and passion about her ideas that were unshakable. "Oddly enough, the most difficult person in the world to love is ourselves and yet it is the most important because only by loving ourselves are we truly our 'self'."

"Wow, I know what you mean." Karl agreed realizing how powerful her words were at the same time.

"It's hard enough to envelop ourselves in love. So when young children are abandoned or lack that feeling of being loved, it feels virtually impossible for them to wrap themselves in their own love. What do they learn to do for love? They first go to the outside sources before seeing the beauty and love for themselves." Her soul gleamed through her eyes as she spoke.

"That's quite a dynamic of forces and characters," Karl told her. "The perfectly beautiful model with the raging inner conflicts and troubles like abandonment and not feeling loved. Most people never think that they don't feel good enough. What other kinds of inner demons do you think people carry?"

"Most women are actually fighting inner self-condemnation, and other kinds of unrealistic self-expectations that stem from the outside world. That's why we need to have an equal focus on our inside worlds, on who we are, and how we experience ourselves in the world."

Karl asked her if this process was just limited to women, or if men had similar experiences.

"Sure they do," she responded on a dime. "Men have equal, though different, societal pressures to look good, to make money and to always be strong." Pointing to people paddling canoes around the lake, Clarissa laughed and said, "We're both in the same boat, you know."

He concurred with Clarissa about the need for more emphasis on his own inner experiences, and shared with her his ingrained focus on work accomplishments, which were always based in the future, as well as on manipulations of the outside world.

Although Clarissa had no problem with people creating the kind of lifestyles they desired, she stressed the fact that becoming too caught up in our surroundings and our appearances only fed the inner demons who wanted to keep us preoccupied with the outer world while they consumed our true inner lives.

"It sounds like you're saying that when we rely on the outside world to tell us who we are, and how we should feel about ourselves," Karl said to Clarissa, "that's when the demons take over."

"Yes, but we're instructed all along, from the moment we step into this world, to take society's view as our own. So we've really got to work to wake up and realize how to change it." She paused to gather her thoughts. "But when we begin to listen to ourselves, the demons and the negative self-talk lose their grip on us. Then, the person that you always wanted to be can finally be revealed. That's when you begin the self love and personal enveloping begins."

Karl was captivated by her words and the inner beauty that came through Clarissa.

"By developing and *enveloping* a process that liberates you from the negativity and connects you with the powerful energy you have inside, you can abolish the demons at any time. You can master the self-esteem regimen of strength and utilize the new self-love and personal power this creates to attain complete balance. When this happens, you naturally look better, you feel better, and you can actually be a better person. Because, then, who you are is who you say you are, not someone else. By enveloping yourself, your true potential is reached."

Meeting Clarissa foreshadowed Karl's inner awakening on Mount Kilimanjaro. She pointed him in the right direction. And though he traveled thousands of miles to reach it, he discovered that the direction was really just inside himself.

Karl enjoyed the warmth of the sun and the vantage point from which he viewed his life and his own inner self. He knew that every encounter he'd had with other people had been a gift newly realized.

Zanzibar
CHAPTER 17

Bridging THE GAP

After a blissful day, Karl attended a musical performance featuring a traditional band from Zanzibar. Sitting on the bed in his hotel room afterwards, he realized that he still hadn't heard from Liz. He gave benefit to the time difference and relaxed his mind as he contemplated the music. He reviewed the melodies as the songs echoed inside him. He thought about how music connected him to his heart, and to a whole panorama of feelings, which only came about through moments of inspiration. Lying back on the bed, Karl had a flash of appreciation for experiences which connected him with his heart.

Thinking about how these experiences came into his life, Karl remembered an old friend who went by the name

Steve "Stealth" Miller, with whom he was no longer in communication.

Actually they had met doing business, but became friends for a year or so before he moved away. He remembered Stealth well, because he was such an avid proponent of living a life filled with heart.

Bridging the Gap

Stealth had a muscular physique and his eyes were exceedingly bright. When he looked at you, it felt like his energy went right through you. If people can be compared to light bulbs, Stealth had about 100 more watts than most others. And he put all his extra voltage to good use. His life purpose was centered on the heart, and how to help others bring awareness of the heart into their lives. He referred to this as the Heartmind.

"Most people live and die without ever bridging the gap between their hearts and their minds," Stealth once told Karl, "between what they think they believe about life and what they really, truly know about being alive. But the truth is, ninety percent of what we know, what we experience, and what we think is in our heartmind."

Karl loved the new perspective and was open to what Stealth meant.

"The idea that we think only with our heads or our brains is a relatively new one, Karl. The mind is not an exclusive component of the brain, it's a greater source, and it's more sympathetic to the heart than any other part of us. That's why I call the most intelligent part of us the heartmind. It's the part that's responsible for most of the decisions and choices we make. It's also connected to our true desires and longings, so it makes an excellent guide for determining what we want in life and how we will try to get it."

Stealth's ideas about the heartmind really interested Karl. Although he wasn't entirely sure what he was talking about, it was easy to see by how he lived that his ideas were related to the energetic integrity that coursed through him in his daily life. He was highly intelligent, expressive and compassionate. And just watching Stealth as he interacted with his environment was inspiring enough to know that he had a special gift.

Over time, Stealth helped Karl to understand that most people are not aware of their true beliefs, whether honest or sincere, because their thinking is disconnected from their deeper truth. One way to discover what you really believe, he showed him, was to look at the fruit of life, because whatever is truly believed in the heartmind will manifest all around. There's a contradiction between what people say they believe and what they really believe.

"When your conscious thoughts are not aligned with your deeper, inner beliefs, there is a contradiction that creates either paralysis or chaos in your life," Stealth told him. "And you can't live a very productive or enjoyable life that way. So it's important to seek a way to know what you truly believe about yourself, the world, and your life. Most people don't know how a belief becomes a belief, so they are powerless to change it. That's why it's such an important thing to learn."

Stealth had a great passion for helping people take the journey inward, for helping them learn how to become aware of their beliefs, and to become connected with their hearts. He believed that once the mind became centered in the heart, an alignment developed between one's conscious thoughts, and one's deeper beliefs, intentions and desires, enabling a person to live the fullest life possible.

"There are many indicators that reveal your inner attitude, like how you feel about people that already have what you want. Can you celebrate their achievements with them and be happy for them in what they have attained? If so, then you have the same beliefs inside yourself that will help you to do the same with your own life. But if you have cynicism, resentment or jealously about others having what you want, then chances are you are holding onto inner beliefs that are counter-productive to actually getting what you want."

Over and again, Stealth emphasized the importance of bridging the gap between the mind and the heart. He suggested various ways to experience the heartmind. One was daydreaming. He encouraged Karl to fantasize about goals and dreams, and to imagine how living and experiencing dreams would feel.

"You want to bridge the gap, to create congruency between your heart and your mind, between the life you long to live and the one you actually are living. You do this by creating a conscious congruency between your inner beliefs and your daily thinking."

As Karl sat in his hotel room and thought of Stealth, he noted the gap that still lingered within him. While it decreased in size throughout the years and as a result of the people he had met along the way and the life had lived, he couldn't help but question the last bit. Stealth was right. The gap needed to be bridged.

Just then he heard a noise outside his door. He wrote it off as the guests mingling. But, something sounded strangely familiar. A woman's voice was getting closer.

Before she could knock at the door, Karl rushed and opened it. Standing before him was Liz as stunning as ever.

She laughed. "How did you know?!"

"Ah, baby, I know your voice. I thought it was my supreme visualization that brought you here."

"It was your heart, Karl." She held onto him. "It was your heart."

Zanzibar
CHAPTER 18

Own YOUR RIGHT

Karl was ecstatic to spend the entire night with his bride. After twenty years, she still felt so new to him.

"Do you know how much I missed you?" He glimmered like a high school boy.

"And I you?!"

"I still can't believe you came all this way. How did you keep this from me? You can't keep a secret to save your life!"

"Well, I guess I can now!"

"So, how's Jake? What's happening at home?"

"I want to hear about you! I want to hear about the climb. What was it like? What were the people like? Was it hard?"

"We've got plenty of time for that. For now I just want to hear about you and home." He smiled warmly and embraced her again.

She gave in. "Well, Jake is so excited and I can't help but cry every time I walk by his room."

"Ah, I know."

"How did it go by so fast, Karl?"

They both sat silent for a moment until Liz broke the quiet. "Oh! And I met this woman on the plane."

"Oh, yeah?"

"Her name was Mali Digius. She's Persian and she's exquisite!"

"Wow! I can't tell if you were more excited to see me or meet her."

"Oh stop!" She nudged him.

"So. Tell me about her." He pushed.

"Ok, so we're sitting on the plane. And I'm in the middle of her and another woman. I was so thankful when I sat down because they both seemed nice enough and you know how long this flight is." He nodded. "But, I was wrong. At least about the woman on my right."

"What happened?"

"First it started with, 'the air is too cold' then it was, 'they don't give us enough leg space on these damn flights' then the coffee was too hot, the chairs were too itchy and next . . . my perfume was too strong."

"But, you don't wear perfume."

"I know!"

"Well after about twenty more complaints, not only did I have enough, but apparently the woman to my left wasn't going to listen to it anymore either."

"Did she say something?"

"In the most calm, manufactured voice she said, 'Did you know that complaining disturbs your cells?'"

"Huh?"

"Yes! It was beautiful. She couldn't have said it more nicely."

"So, what did the other woman say?" Karl was very interested now.

"Well, her face finally softened since the start of the flight and she said, 'excuse me?'" Liz couldn't tame her animation. "So, Mali said to her, 'pardon my intrusion but it seems like such a shame to cause yourself so much stress. You have these wonderful cells that are working for you, fighting for you and keeping you healthy and to cause so much stress over minute things just creates an enemy within yourself. It disturbs your cells.'"

"Is that true?" Karl was curious now.

"It makes perfect sense to me, because listen to what else she said."

"What?"

"I was so intrigued with what she had to say that I probed her for more information. She simply told me that I should own my right."

"Own your right?"

"Sounds funny. But, as she explained I got it. She told me that you realize your right through education and experience. You realize what your core values are and you live by those principles. When you think right, you act right and you talk right. You have this incredible freedom when you live by your right. When you don't, you lose that freedom."

"So, she's saying that when you live by your right and stay true to your core values, you feel free."

"Right."

"Not a whole lot of reason to complain then, right?"

"Bingo!"

"I like that!" Karl shared in her joy.

"I knew you would."

"What'd you say we grab a late night snack and then come back to this romantic little cabana and call it a night?"

"What are we waiting for?"

Karl grabbed his wife and kissed her just before getting up to leave the room.

Zanzibar

CHAPTER 19

A Business FAMILY

Karl had thoroughly enjoyed his vacation off the coast of Zanzibar. The final surprise from Liz was just what he needed. She left early to catch her flight and Karl had still one more day on this island. As the day of his return home approached, he thought more about his business and how it aligned with his personal goals of fulfillment. He reflected on the kind of business he had created and how it had affected the lives of his employees. For no matter how successful his business might become financially, he was increasingly realizing the human aspect of his operation, since interacting with all of these new faces and remembering those of the past. In essence, there would be no business without human beings there would be no relationships without connection. Karl was becoming more aware of the preciousness of each human life.

Sitting in a tropical garden near the cliffs, Karl opened his journal to view the recollections of his encounters. Of the many he wrote along his journeys, he noticed that one page was left.

On the last day before Karl would return home he met John Donan, a high-ranking executive with a very lucrative firm, who was preparing for the next day's family safari trip. Karl told him about the experiences he had along the climb. But, unlike any of the others staying at the hotel intrigued by his physical climbing experience, John was disinterested in the climb and asked him, "And what of the people?"

"Well, I met amazing people on this journey."

"And?" John pushed.

"And… they were great!" Karl was at a loss for more words and he could tell John wanted more.

John just sat and smiled at Karl. He had a very humorous way about him, but Karl started to feel a bit awkward and didn't know whether this was intentional or not. John seemed at complete ease with a smile on his face. They sat for a few moments, each of them sipping their iced tea. Karl looked around and began to count the hours till it was time to leave. John just remained seated as comfortable as ever, grinning.

Finally Karl broke, "Is there something wrong?"

"Let me ask you something Karl," John asked, ignoring Karl's question.

"Ok."

"You say you own a business?"

"Yes, I do."

"I assume you do well."

"It does amazing. But, it took many lessons learned to arrive here."

"And do you feel that you have arrived?"

"I... Well, of course, I mean. Yes, I think I've done a good job at--"

"Do you feel completely and totally fulfilled?"

"I'm not sure what you're getting at."

"What do your friends say about you?"

"They like me."

"And your wife? She loves you?"

"She's amazing. I've never felt more love from anyone."

"Your son?"

"Yeah, him too. I'm sorry John, but I'm not quite sure what you're trying to ask me."

"Karl, I could tell right away that you are one hundred percent fulfilled in your personal relationships. And as far as making money goes, you seem more than all right. I gather you like your career and you get a sense of victory and pride when you do well. You seem to be able to afford the luxuries of life and you appear to be relatively happy.

What do the people you work with say about you? Do they give you those same fulfilling feelings as your family or your friends?"

Karl was a bit taken aback by this and told him he thought his employees and colleagues regarded him fairly well, and that he appreciated them and demonstrated as much by paying them a very competitive wage.

John chuckled slyly and made Karl feel even worse and more confused. "It's nice that you do that," he replied. "But having an invested interest and a positive regard for your employees is more complex than what you pay them. You realize that you spend more hours with those you work with on most days than you spend with your own family?"

"Uh huh."

Karl's mind started again with the volcano of questions. Family? Work? Combined?

John continued, overcoming Karl's loud thoughts. "What if you thought about the people you work with as if they were your family? What if work wasn't just about the gain?"

Karl had to think about that for a minute. "Hmm. Don't you think that might invite disaster, by getting too close to the people you work with? I mean I do believe in treating them well and I've known several people that do treat their employees as family, but I just worry that it might cause some unnecessary drama."

"Sure, it could. You've got to have boundaries with them as well, just as you do with yourself in personal relationships. But when you're at work, and you're all focusing on an overall group goal, you really are working together as one big family. Treating your employees as if they were family is just another way of saying that you are all essentially interconnected and subject to a similar fate, in terms of the future of your business. And the more connected you feel to your employees, the more inspired you will be to interact and accomplish work tasks too."

"Ok. I see what you're getting at now."

"You completed the climb, which is an endeavor worth celebrating and praising yourself for. But, I still wonder about the people."

"You know I really connected with some of them. In fact, if it weren't for them I don't know that I could have completed the climb. Some of them might have been more worthy of the experience."

John smiled.

Karl thought about applying John's advice to his employees and colleagues. He knew it would imbue his business with a sense of caring and warmth that might have been previously lacking due to his reluctance. But, what a foundation it would create when and if business was struggling. Treating employees like equals, being empathic, and taking their concerns into consideration would help him to envision a larger collective purpose for his business, which would make achieving specific goals easier.

Karl was getting excited to return home and get back to work. He suddenly saw it as a kind of professional nourishment in which they could all feed one another. It took time for Karl to reach the place where he could trust another on a personal level and allow himself to grow and accept support. He found this with Liz. Their family became a system of love and support that nourished each other, not only through what they did, but by how they acted toward one other.

As a leader, Karl realized he was responsible to set the tone for the group dynamics at work. Just as principles based on integrity, trust, perseverance and commitment worked to keep a family unit strong, they would work to keep a group of people striving toward a common goal.

John's daughter, son and wife came to the table to greet him and steal him away from Karl. Karl watched their smiles and in that moment Karl realized that while reaching the summit and making it to the peak was an immeasurable feeling of overwhelming pride, the moments that he would always treasure were the conversations.

Karl flipped through his journal. In looking at all the people he had met in his life, one thing stood out now that never stood before. One answer to the question that pondered his mind for a long time came to surface in that moment and gave him that extra added peace he sought. It's the missing part to bridge the gap.

While he conquered many battles along the way through the messages brought to him by friends, family and even strangers, there was one common thread among the messages that he wasn't quite applying yet. With each message came a purpose.

Karl closed his journal and took a moment to breathe in the fresh, fragrant scent of tropical plants and flowers all around him. Sitting in the chair, exuding an overwhelming appreciation for the garden universe that surrounded him, he realized that sometimes life is unforgiving, like a mountain. The steps taken must be walked slowly to successfully make it to the top. But, in the end, the only real purpose in life is to live for the purpose of really living.

Climbing Mt. Kilimanjaro achieved more for Karl than a physical feat. The reflections and interactions he experienced with the others were brought to the surface and applied. Whether it was the change of climate, the mental focus or the appreciation for his life, Karl felt more aligned with each message he had received throughout his life. With ease, he applied each one to his life.

One year after climbing Mt. Kilimanjaro, Karl humbly accepted an award for the highest performing green building company for commercial properties.

Oddly enough, the climb to his victory had been his easiest yet.

Co-Author Biographies

Clarissa Burt is a TV/Video producer, public speaker, author, writer, inventor, award-Winning actress and entertainer. She was a top model for cosmetic houses such as Revlon, Dior, and Clarita, Helena Rubenstein and her selection as the worldwide "Face" for Orlane Cosmetics. Clarissa has performed in numerous movies and can be remembered as Xayide in "The Never Ending Story, part II," and as Guilia in the award-winning "Caruso Pascosky". Clarissa has also appeared on hundreds of television shows. Her television productions have included The Miss Universe Pageant and World Sports Awards. She is the developer of Clarissa Burt Hair Product and Facial Cream Lines. A leading authority on beauty, image, and self-esteem, "Good Morning, Italy" called upon Clarissa to host the popular beauty segment, "Clarissa Suggests. After 25 years in Europe, she returned to the United States to host her own radio show "Clarissa Burt Talks." She was chosen health and beauty editor for Runway Magazine's 2008 launch. Clarissa is currently launching ClarissaBurtLive. TV, "The Look Good, Feel Good, Be Good" television for women. Ms. Burt's book "The Self Esteem Regime", focused on the betterment and empowerment of women is due for a summer 2011 release. Clarissa Burt can be reached at: **www.ClarissaBurt.com**

Eileen Schwartz is a leader of Business Development and Sales Training. Business Development has been a huge part of what Eileen Schwartz has spent the past 25 years doing with companies, sales professionals and managers all across the US. In addition, Eileen has completed over 3,500 coaching and consulting sessions with top real estate professionals across the country. Having been a top producing real estate agent placing in the top 1%-2% nationwide since 1996, she not only teaches how to be successful; she is a proven leader in the industry. She is a certified coach as well as the owner and founder of Coach2Sell, a powerful coaching company. Having led multiple large franchise real estate companies in their training and professional development divisions, she is a great resource to develop a training division or enhance what you currently have. If you are interested in becoming your business best and working from a place of greatness you will want to contact Eileen Schwartz at: **eileenschwartz@msn.com**

Gerri Kier is a Certified Natural Health Professional and Certified Loomis Digestive Health Specialist and President of Complete Nutrition Alliance. Health and wellness are her life and when not in the office she can be found reading books, working in the garden or hiking mountains. In the health wellness world, Gerri helps clients determine where nutrition deficiencies are in their bodies. Since deficiencies lead to disease, she guides them in the process of gaining optimal health and wellness through proper nutrition support. Education Elevated is a nonprofit Gerri founded in 2008. The first project her hiking / trekking team worked on is a school in the Chyangba Village in Nepal. Prior to health, wellness and hiking she had a 22-year career as a photographer. She finds the past photography experience very handy when trekking the mountains around Colorado and in Nepal. Gerri resides in Colorado with husband Greg and new golden lab, Bailey, and can be contacted at: **gerri@completena.com**

J. Shoop is a professional speaker, author, and mentor, J. Shoop's compelling talks and workshops have made him a highly sought-after leader in the field of personal development. His mission in life is to inspire, educate, and help others to become consciously aware of their unlimited potential for greatness. For more than 20 years, J. has been involved in the study, application, and mastery of the universal principles necessary for achievement and success. He shares his uncommon approach and methods through private mastermind sessions, group coaching programs, and exclusive one-to-one success coaching. His most recent project, The Success Bullseye, is scheduled to be released in the Fall of 2011, and he continues to be looked upon as an invaluable resource to assist others in the further development of their attitude, skills, and character. To connect with J., visit **www.jshoop.com** or send an email to **jshoop@jshoop.com**

John Donan, Jr., is the chairman of Donan Engineering Co., Inc. John, originally from western Kentucky, is a graduate of Texas A & M University with degrees in Geology and Geological Engineering. After a brief stint as a petroleum engineer in west Texas, he served in the U.S. Air Forces as an intelligence office in the Strategic Air Command. He then returned to western Kentucky to work in a family civil and mining engineering firm. In 1987 he sold the Kentucky firm and moved to Indiana where he started a similar firm doing similar work. In 2000 he changed the focus of the firm entirely to forensic engineering and the investigation of origin and cause of fires and explosives. The firm, now based in Louisville, KY, has offices in 18 states. He takes pride in knowing that, while the firm is a family business, each employee is an honored member of the business family. John is a registered professional engineer, a registered geologist, and a certified fire investigator. One of his greatest satisfactions comes from mentoring young professionals in his firm and seeing them grow personally and professionally. He is active in various church and civic organizations, and loves wood-working and sailing. John can be reached at **donanjg@gmail.com**

Joyce Alzona is a southern California resident and mother of five. She has dedicated her life towards the betterment of others. She can be reached at: **jcalzona@sbcglobal.net**

Kathy Curtis is a successful real estate agent on the central coast of California who believes life is too short to do something you don't "LOVE". She is passionate about sales, marketing, mentoring people and helping others. This is where she shines as a real estate expert with the past diverse careers she's done she pulls past experiences into her daily career. Kathy has always been extremely motivated, hardworking and determined to be what she wants to be. Heeding her parents advice that, "The sky is the limit Kath," she believes if you're fearless about working hard, being smart, and being a good, honest, ethical, person with integrity, then you're on your way to success! All you can do is the best you can and trust you have done the best you can. Her dear friend Brenda once told her, "Life is Trust, Test and Temporary." Each day, at least one of the "T"s happen, it's up to you to affect how it turns out. Today, Kathy challenges you to show one nice gesture to somebody else. Let her know by email what you did and how it turned out. As she says, "Let go; and Let God." You can connect with Kathy Curtis at 805-550-1073 or **kathycurtishasfaith@gmail.com**

Lee and Nana Hinsley

Lee has been tearing things apart, figuring out how they work, repairing, and putting them back together since the age of four. Never much of a sleeper, he drove his parents crazy making noise until all hours of the night as he "tinkered" on his countless projects in the family garage as a young person. After paying his way through college, and graduating Summa Cum Laude, Lee dove into the workplace, and quickly learned he wanted his own business. As an entrepreneur he calmly continues down the path of enlightenment on a daily basis, enjoying all life has to offer, while thoughtfully conquering the many challenges that business ownership offers. Plastics eventually became his passion, where he has spent his past 20 years pioneering such products as fire retardant sheeting, crawlspace encapsulation films and self-adhesive films with no adhesive. Lee is blessed with a family life that is very fun and fulfilling, and feels his greatest accomplishments come from being a good husband, stepfather, son and brother. Lee can be reached at: **lee@globalplasticsheeting.com**

Nana is best known for her smile and her love for bringing people together to have fun and learn from new experiences and adventures. Nana's skills are diverse. Professionally she comes from a corporate sales background, working for companies like Bausch & Lomb, Phillip Morris, Grubb & Ellis and others. Of late she jumped in with her husband Lee and started Global Plastic Sheeting. This experience, starting a brand new company in the worst economic times (late 2007), has proven to be her proudest accomplishment, next to the close relationship she has with her nuclear family. Who knew she could get their website sizzling, their sales force humming, and their company thriving? Life is about the experience-the challenges that comes along the way in this thing we call life. That is where we have the opportunity to find out who we are, and celebrate our successes and learn from our temporary setbacks. It's all good all the time. It may not always be fun, but it's all good.

For fun just add some sunshine, water (ocean) and great people. Nana is blessed with the most amazing family—the best times always abound when the family and friends are around. She can be reached at: **nana@globalplasticsheeting.com**

Linda Rocco has asked the same questions as many: Who Am I? Where Did I Come From? Why Am I Here? Just How Many Taxes Do I Have To Pay Anyway? Though some are content with their family's traditional response to those questions, she wasn't content. Her insatiable need to find her own answers led her to study ancient civilizations, spiritual belief systems, and cultural practices from around the world. She soon learned that everything she thought was true and real, was only one particular culture's way of thinking, believing, and living life. That's all it was, just one way of living life. She searched for threads of truth that permeate all cultures, and all time periods. She is committed to sharing her findings with the courageous souls who are willing to look beyond the social consciousness into an ever unwinding tapestry of what we call life. For more information you can contact Linda at: **linda@hotrockjewelry.com or lindarocco337@gmail.com**

Luba S. Rusyn is a business promoter. She is a diverse industry entrepreneurial success. In 1993 she supplemented her business wisdom with formal knowledge by earning a Bachelor of Commerce degree. Her success can be attributed to her ability to translate this combination of knowledge and wisdom into efficient and effective results. Her enchantment with business spans 30 years, from the family farm, where she became skilled at production and bartering product price with wholesalers (Sunkist) to large organizations such as the Edmonton Oilers Hockey Club (1984-85 Stanley Cup) and Meyers Norris Penny LLP (public accounting). As a business owner/operator (elk ranching, Laundromats, dental offices, coaching/consulting), Luba understands entrepreneurial challenges and thus provides her clients with objective and actionable advice that promotes their success. You can reach Luba at: **luba@rsp360.com**

Margaret Ziedin is known as a business mentor and trusted friend. She is a General Manager for a retail development project. Originally from Sydney, Australia she is an accomplished international entrepreneur. Margaret's formula for success teaches and inspires others to courageously embrace their true-life purpose. Her bold and globally resourceful style attracts masterminds in the making, who she likes to partner with in business ventures. Her firm belief that motivation and passion become most rewarding when we give all of ourselves to the benefit others brought Margaret to amazing feats. In 2010 Margaret raced in the half distance (70.3) Silverman Nevada known as the "World's Toughest Triathlon" with her true prize being the 3rd greatest fundraiser for *Challenged Athletes Foundation's® (CAF) Operation Rebound® The* program provides unparalleled sports opportunities and support to American active military service members and veterans of any branch, and first responders (past and present) who have suffered permanent physical injuries. While embracing the sport of triathlon, Margaret and her friends organized www.meetup.com/TRIbeLV . The groups objective drives members to **TRI be** all they can be through triathlon and to champion philanthropic causes as they race. Get in touch with Margaret at: **margaret@ziedin.com**

Mali Digius is an entrepreneur, business owner, jewelry designer, philanthropist, teacher, wife, mother and grandmother. She is nothing short of remarkable. Originally, Ms. Digius was educated as a college math and science schoolteacher in her native Iran. After fleeing Iran following the regime change in 1980, Mrs. Digius immigrated to the United States with great hardship. To support her family Mrs. Digius tried her hand at odd jobs such as babysitting and selling encyclopedias. Thereafter, in 1984, with only four hundred dollars in her pocket she began to sell jewelry to friends and soon discovered she had a knack for sales. As her business began to boom, she and her husband opened a retail jewelry store, Diamond Boutique, in San Diego, California and operated it as a family business. Over the next twenty-seven years, Mali and her family continued to grow their business and expanded into Del Mar, California. Today, due to her perseverance and determination, Diamond Boutique is one of the most prominent and exclusive jewelry stores in southern California. Mali can be reached at: **www.diamondboutiqueonline.com**

Michele Massion initiated her career in real estate in 1989 and has been the top producer in sales and volume of residential real estate properties ever since. She is currently working for Real Living Lifestyles Real Estate in San Diego County. Understanding that prosperity comes with hard work and dedication, Michele continuously works hard to reach her financial goals with self-motivation. Michele uses the challenges of the real estate business to grow in knowledge and skill. Whether it's a first-time client or a seasoned buyer, she makes the client her priority. Along with the joys of real estate, Michele finds time to go sailing, golfing, dancing or taking long walks on the beach near her home or spending time with her talented son. You can reach her at: 760-455-8257 or by email at **realtormichele@gmail.com**

Richard Barrier read *Think and Grow Rich* in 1977. He was twenty years old. In 1978, he started his corporate career working with large computer systems. Since then he has been laid off twice in 1993 and in 2003, just four days before leaving for Peru. A dream he had since he was twenty, Richard went anyway. In June 2009, Richard started his first business. Six weeks later he was told that the department was being shutdown and that his last day was September 30th. On September 10th he received an e-mail about a *Think and Grow Rich: Three Feet From Gold* event just five miles from where he lived. Richard did not know any of the speakers but that October event changed his life. On January 2011, he started his second business. Richard took his specialized knowledge of computer languages and applied it to smartphones, he hired himself. Over the Top Projects LLC is a software development company focused on parental controls of smartphones. You can contact Richard at: **ikebanaman@yahoo.com**

Ruthe St-Pierre's life has been varied and filled with growing experiences. She was born in war-stricken Angola, where at a young age she learned to not be defeated by events and circumstances and to continue fighting for her dreams and what is important in life. After moving to Canada, serving in the Canadian military, getting a Psychology Bachelor Degree and holding a consulting and management position in a resume company, Ruthe focused on being Queen of the home to her husband and their four children. During those years she also ran successful home-based businesses. Ruthe now resides in the United States with her family. After the real estate market collapse, she got involved in real estate, as her motto is: "When everyone gets out, it's time to get in!" Ruthe is passionate about sharing her many life experiences and the lessons learned from them. She writes for her own pleasure and trains, educates, coaches and mentors individuals to follow their passions and dreams, taking them to the next level. She has learned that when life gives you challenges "You either remain bitter or become better!" Ruthe chooses better! She can be reached at: **ruthe@ruthestpierre.com**

Steven Kaufman, CPA is a principal in Zeus Mortgage where he has coordinated over a billion dollars in real estate financing for companies like American Express, Hewlett Packard, and Exxon Mobil. Zeus Mortgage is the 37th fastest growing private financial service firms in the US according to Inc. Magazine. Steven is frequently interviewed by local and national news organizations like FOX, ABC, CBS, CNN, and Bloomberg on the current financial markets. Steven is an inductee into the business honorary Beta Gamma Sigma and a former Honorary Chairman of the Business Advisory Council of the National Republican Congressional Committee. National Mortgage Professional Magazine recently ranked Steven as one of the "Top 40 Most Influential Mortgage Professionals in the United States" and he is a United States Ernst & Young Entrepreneur of the Year Finalist. Steven is a World Bench Press Champion and he is a co-founder and current President of The Fanatical Change Foundation. Steven can be reached at 713-ASK-ZEUS (275-9387) or **steven@askzeus.com**

Steve "Stealth" Miller is one of the most interesting and powerful men you will ever meet. With an extremely diverse arsenal of talents, gifts, and achievements, He is able to move seamlessly among the worlds of entertainment, corporate, and ministry. His presentations are riveting and life changing, characterized by a high level of energy and a wealth of knowledge and experience that comes from a decorated career as a world-class martial arts fighter/professional strength athlete. He is an inspiration for people to live life and live it big. His favorite expression is "If you're going to be a bear, be a grizzly ... anything else is just another bear!" That belief is evident in every area of his life; 29 years of marriage to his wife Mary, three successful children, two grandchildren, dozens of informally adopted kids around the country that call him and Mary mom & dad, and an extraordinary life and career as "America's Favorite Life Coach." He has earned fourth degree black belts in Tae Kwon Do and Hap Ki Do as well as a first-degree black belt in Ju Jit Su. His various disciplines of martial arts have helped him to be a champion fighter in Mixed Martial Arts competitions. He has trained dozens of professional athletes to become world champions. He has spoken to over a million young people around the world through school assemblies, conferences, and demonstrations. He currently holds four world records including a recent feature on Ripley's Believe it or Not" television program; a young lady jumped off of a 27-story tower, attached only to a bungee cord. Steve stood on top of the building and held the other end of the cord with his bare hands. Steve is also the founder of **The EOT, (**The Embassy of Transformation) a non-profit foundation that teaches young people the principles of success through **"The Leadership Academy."** Steve is the author of numerous books and DVD projects including, **"Chick magnets, The Focus factor, The Laws of Extraordinary Living, Bring Your 'A' Game,** and **Principles and Strategies of a World Champion."** His signature message, **"Personal Renovation ... Building from the Inside Out,"** is in great demand around the world. He is a featured expert on the new hit movie **"Pass It On."** His literary works have been published in "**Personal Development**" magazine as well as numerous e-zines. You can reach Steve at: **stevestealthmiller@gmail.com** or www.stevestealthmiller.com

Tish Taylor is originally from a small town in Idaho has become an accomplished entrepreneur. Tish's success is in encouraging others and believing there is strength in failure. As a professional cheerleader, she served as captain pioneering community, national awareness and support for the North America's National Lacrosse League (NLL). Her favorite parts were the friendships developed with season ticket holders. Her warm heartedness and perseverance resulted in a successful career and her talent for maintaining a close network of business relationships had her finishing in the top 10% of her colleagues over 10 consecutive years in the pharmaceutical and biotech industry. Letting go of the corporate hustle, Tish decided to evolve her business acumen into a partnership with a new company, her vast network and client base and founded 'Bay Area Healthcare Consulting', with a focus in a collaborative partnerships that highlights healthcare as passion for prevention, not a system of fixes. Bay Area Healthcare Consulting believes in the difference demonstrated. Find out more at **650-430-1223** or email Tish at: **latishataylor@hotmail.com**